Primary Concepts

Cover Design
Elliot Kreloff, Inc.

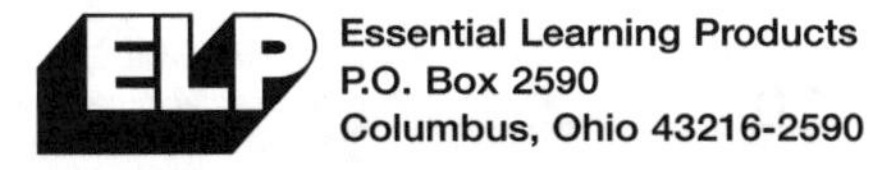

Essential Learning Products
P.O. Box 2590
Columbus, Ohio 43216-2590

The text in this book originally appeared in *Math Practice Book—Counting & Measuring, Telling Time, Basic Facts*
©1992 Essential Learning Products

Printed in the United States of America
10 9 8 7 6 5 4 3 2

INTRODUCTION

Math Practice Simplified—Primary Concepts is exactly what the title says. It is practice presented in its most direct and simplified form. Practice reinforces skills and allows children to use math effectively. However, children develop an *understanding* of math concepts by exploring and investigating. Opportunity to work with concrete models and other formal instruction techniques must be provided to children *before* this book is used. That is, teaching of each concept must precede the practice activities provided.

Math Practice Simplified—Primary Concepts is designed to increase understanding of beginning concepts, such as counting, writing numerals, telling time, counting money, measuring, and basic adding and subtracting. Although this book is developmentally appropriate for use as enrichment for five-year-olds and practice for six-year-olds, it can be adapted to serve the needs of other students. Matching these and other materials to each child's ability is critical to success. Individuals require varying amounts of practice to acquire facility, so some children will need to practice these skills far more than others. Just remember that brief daily practice is generally more effective than longer but less frequent practice.

Math Practice Simplified—Primary Concepts may be used in the classroom as a supplement to a basal program, or it may be used at home. Many children will be able to use the book independently after the directions have been read to them and the sample exercises completed with them. As students progress through the book, they gain confidence. The layout of each page is "student-friendly," not intimidating. A variety of activities actively involve the learner in counting, writing, drawing, and coloring.

Students who complete this book successfully are likely to build a solid foundation for mathematics, increase self-esteem, and improve performance on standardized tests.

Answers at the back of the book are arranged in the same order as the exercises appear on each individual page. The numerals used in this book are from the Zaner-Bloser Alphabet.

CONTENTS

0 zero

1 one

Circle how many.

0 1

1 0

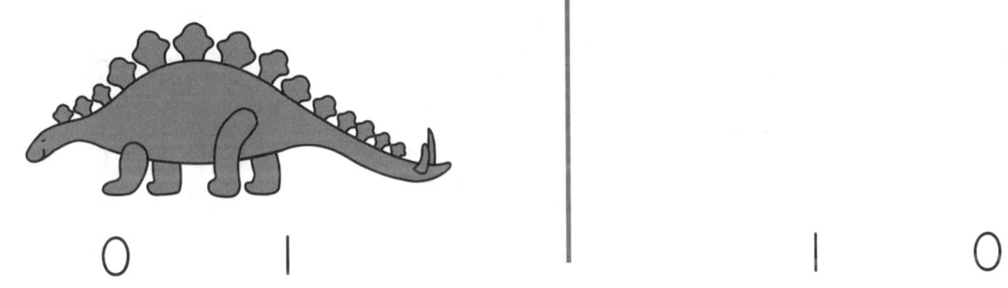

0 1

1 0

Write.

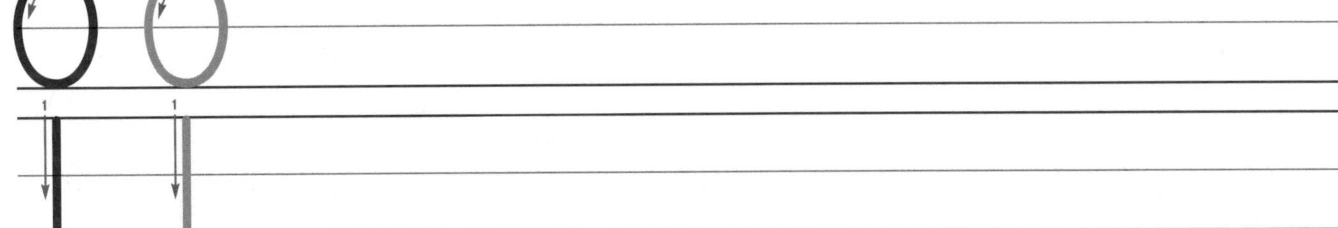

Write how many.

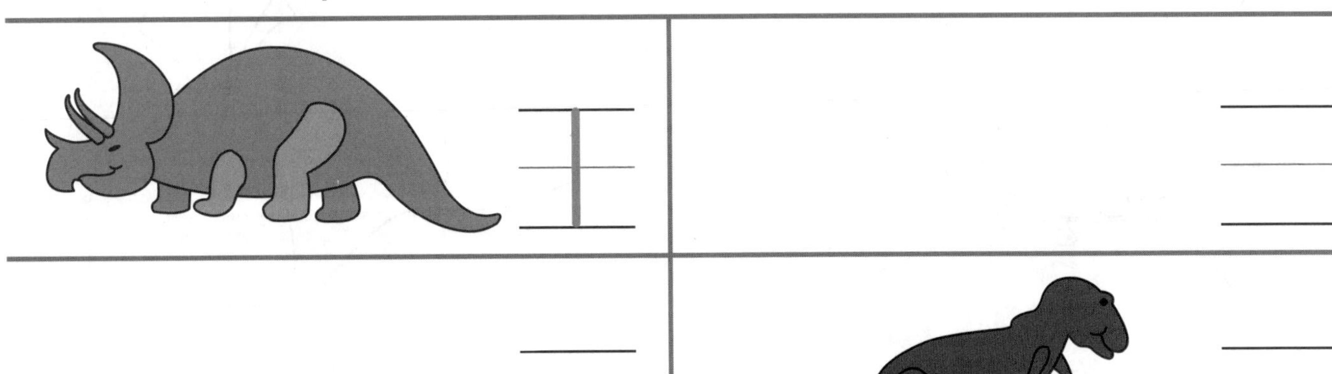

Color the groups with 2. Circle the groups with 3.

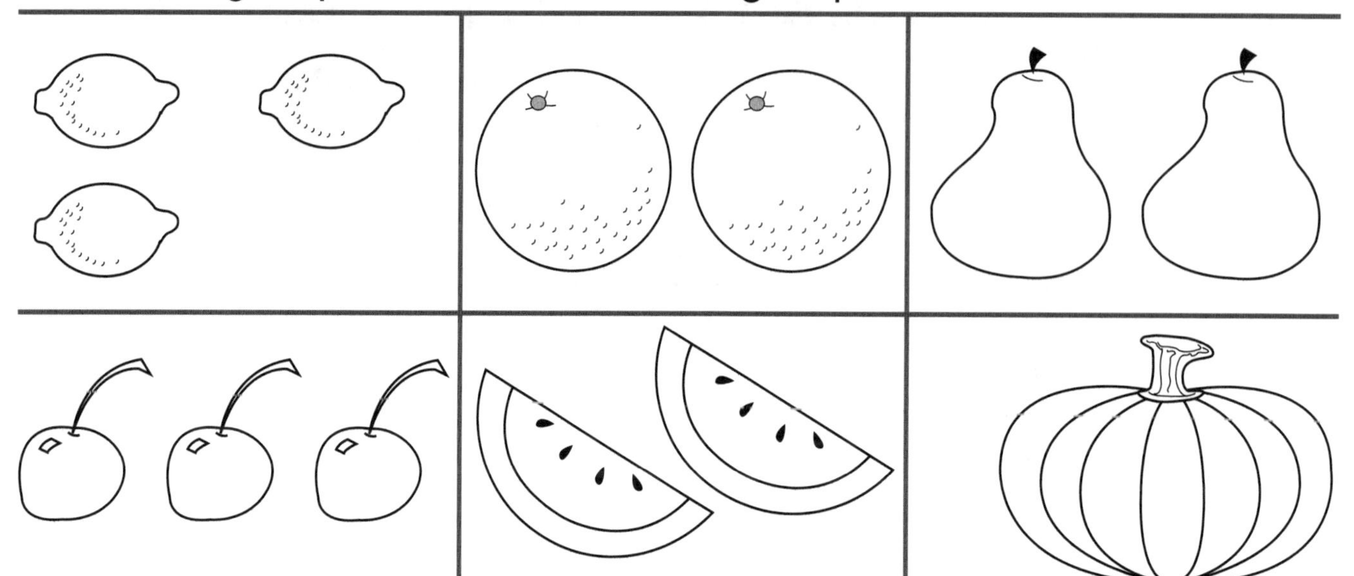

Draw apples to show how many.

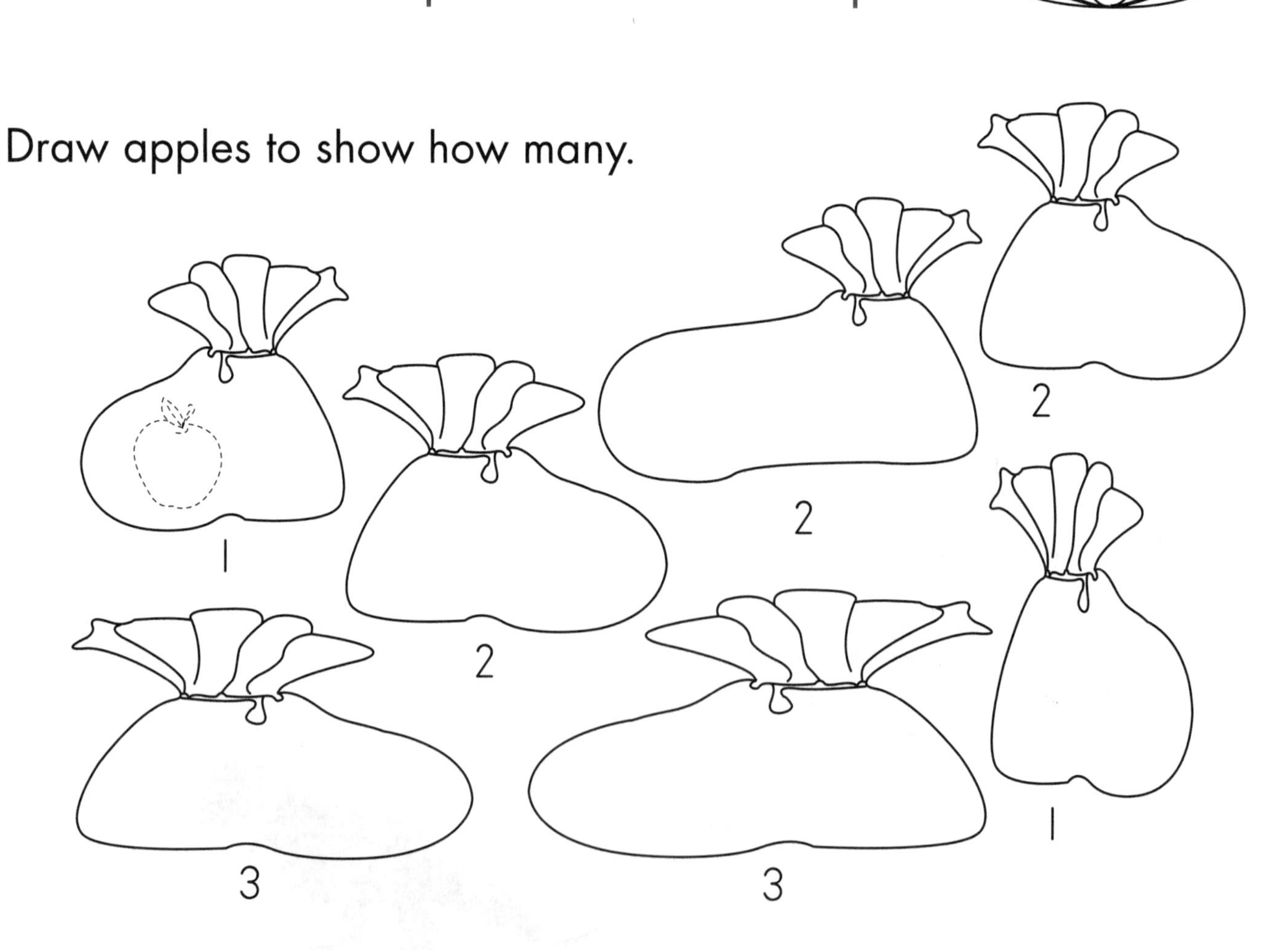

Circle how many.

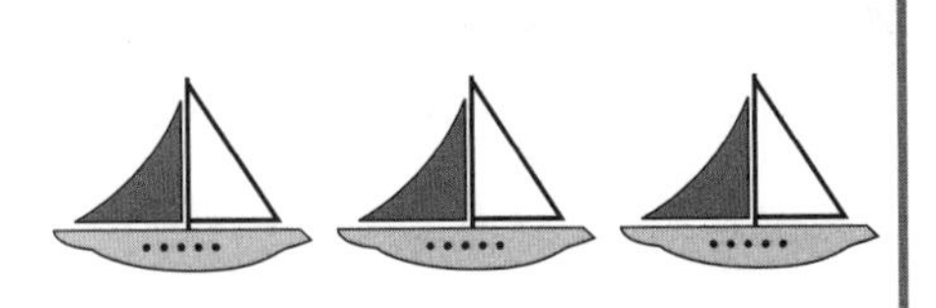

1 2 (3)

2 3 1

3 1 2

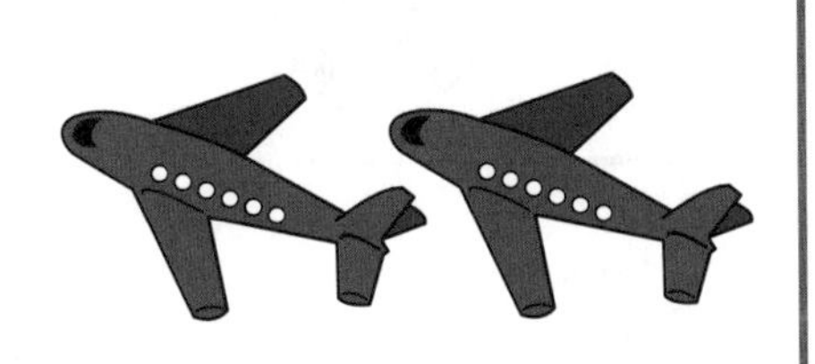

1 3 2

3 2 1

2 1 3

Write.

2 2

3 3

Write how many.

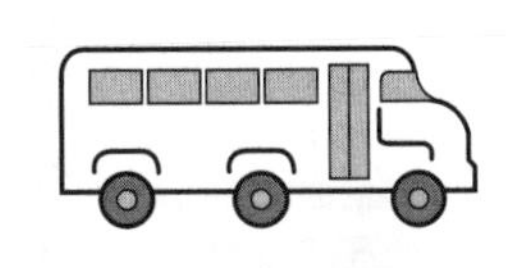

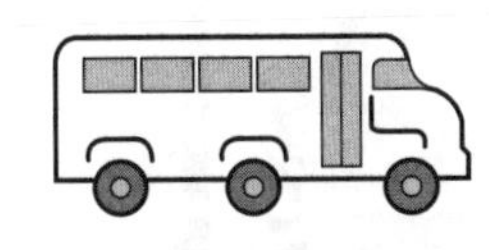

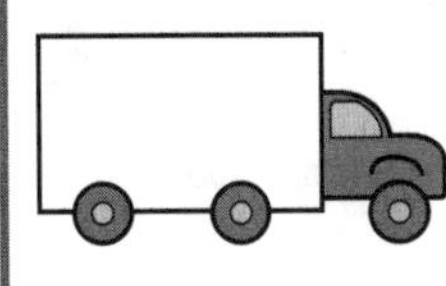

3 three

4 four

Color the groups with 4.

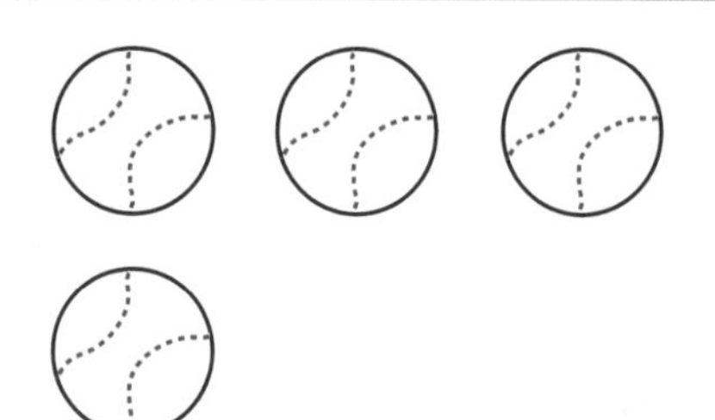

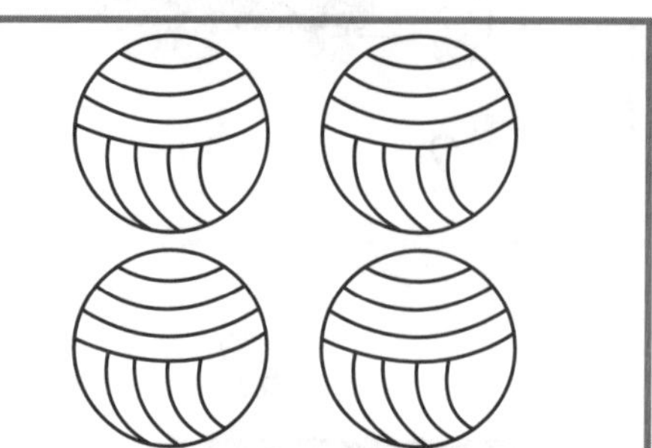

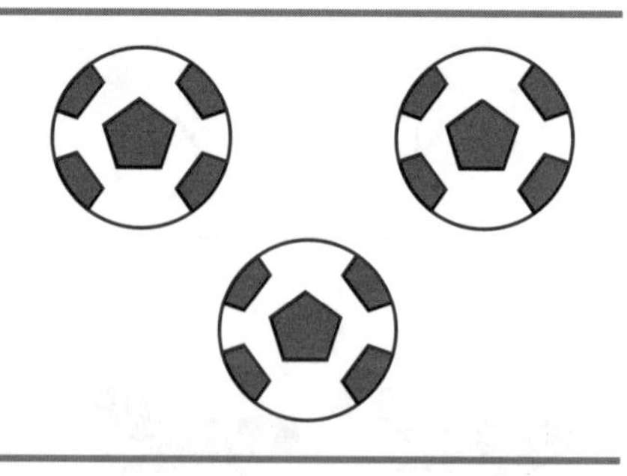

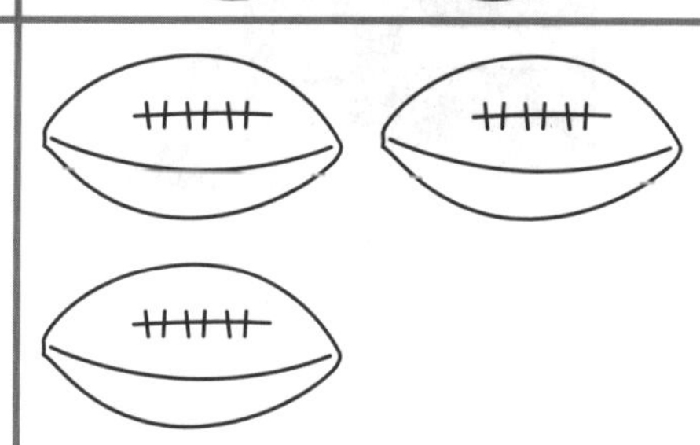

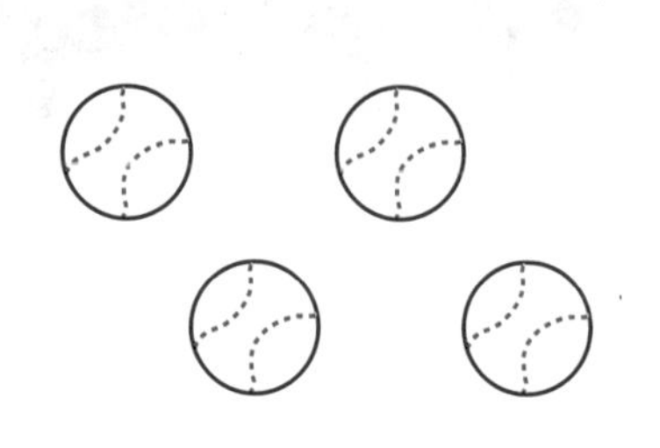

Draw faces to show how many.

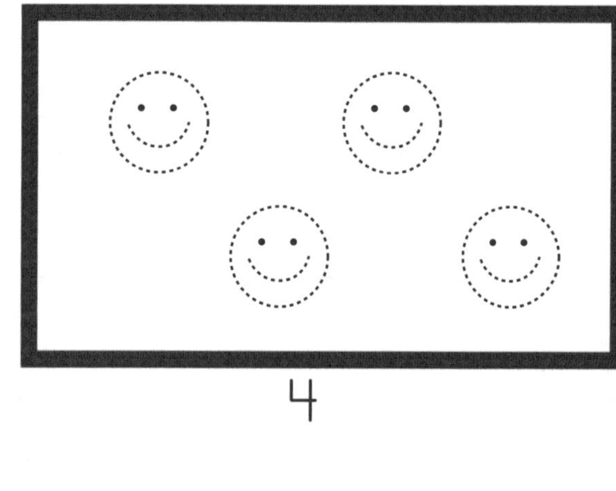

4

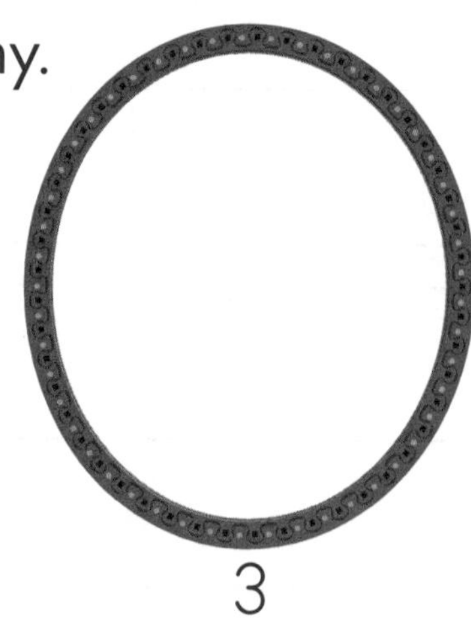

3

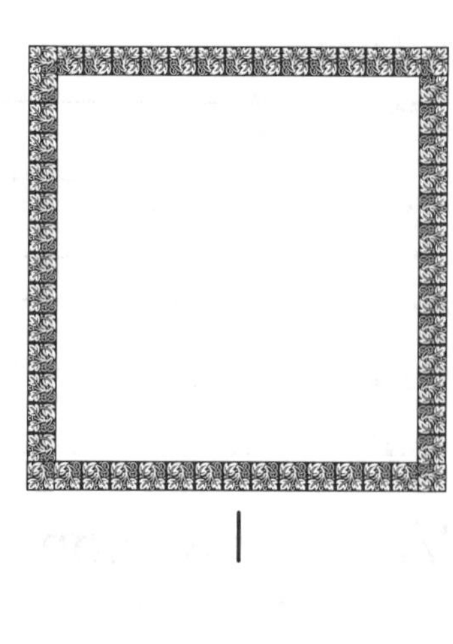

1

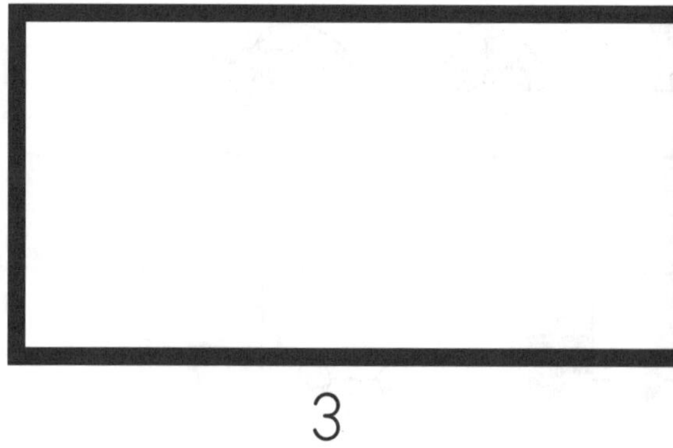

3

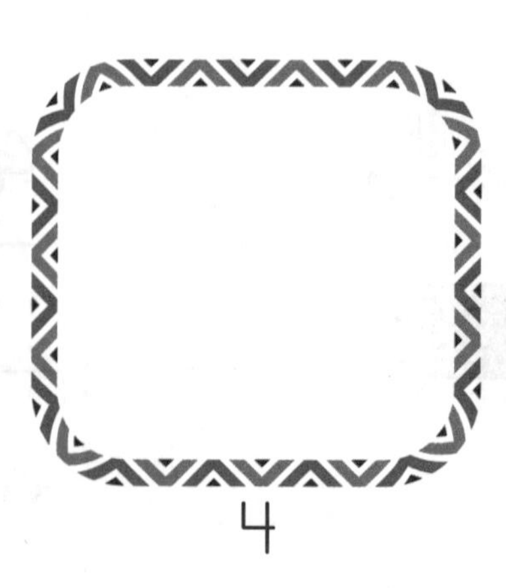

4

2

Circle how many.

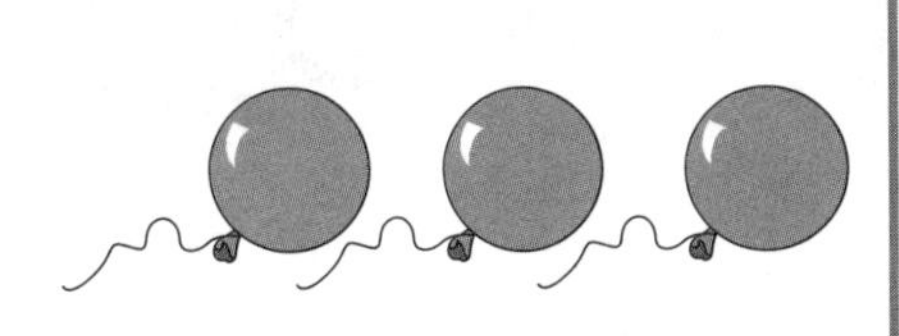

(3) 4

4 3

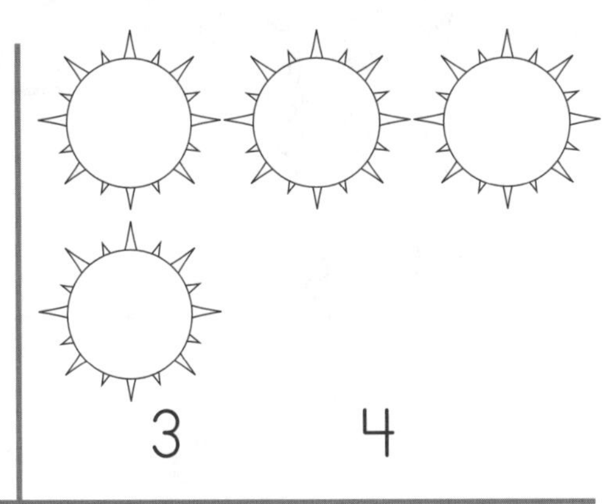

3 4

4 3

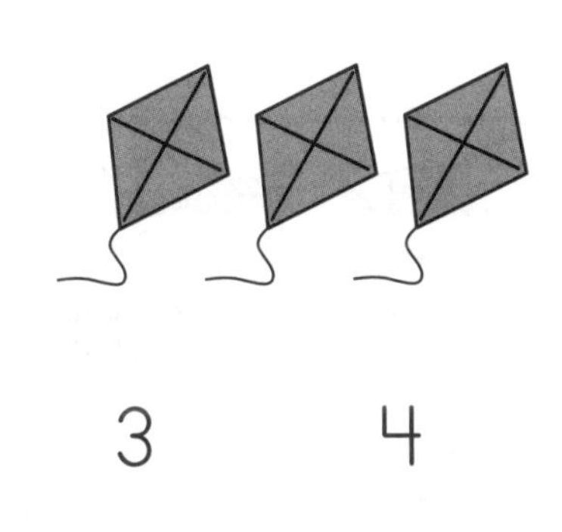

3 4

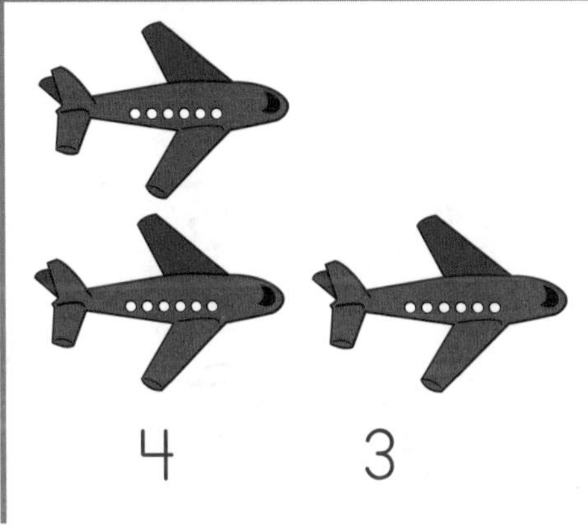

4 3

Write.

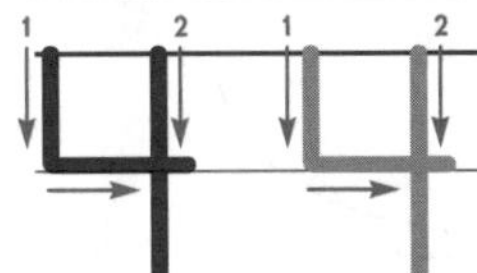

Write how many.

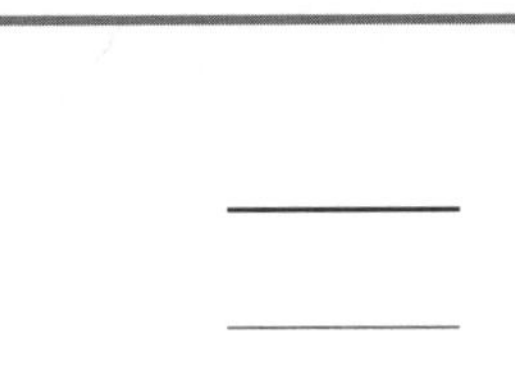

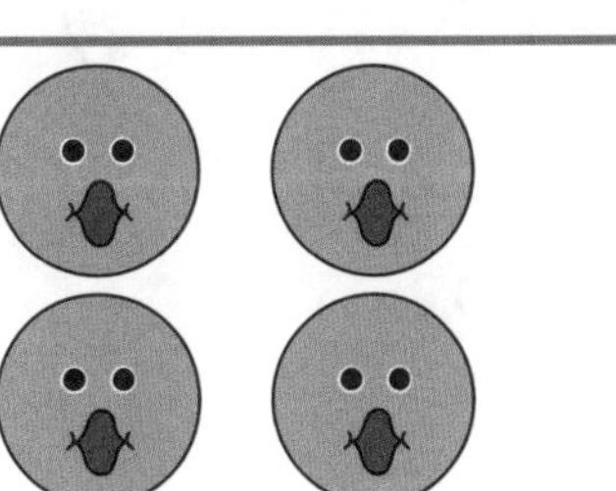

Circle the groups with 5.

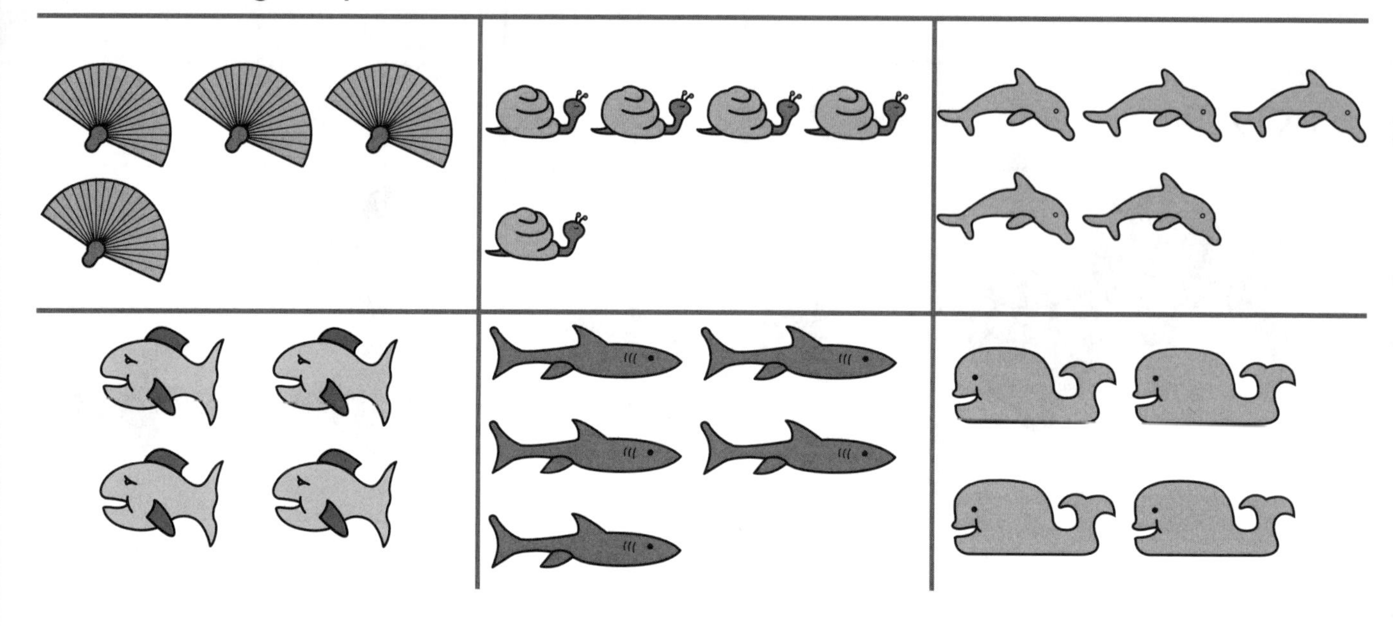

Draw fish to show how many.

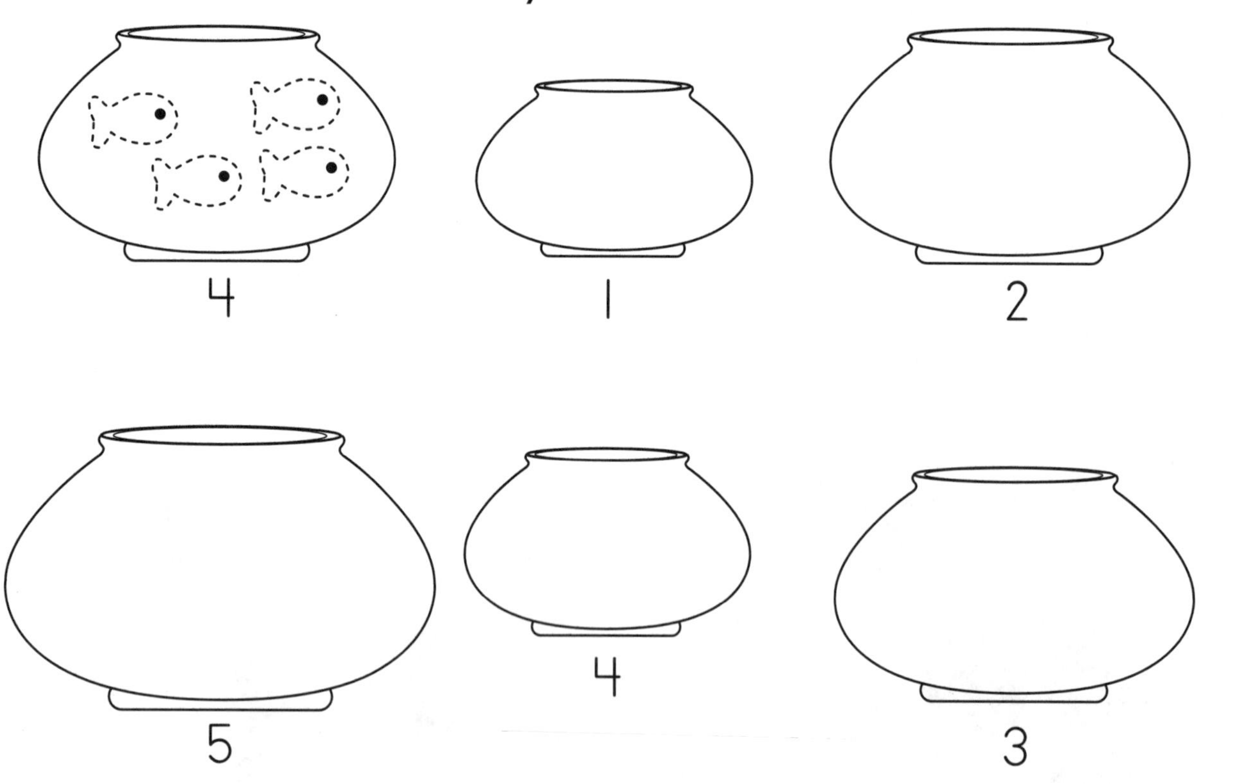

Circle how many.

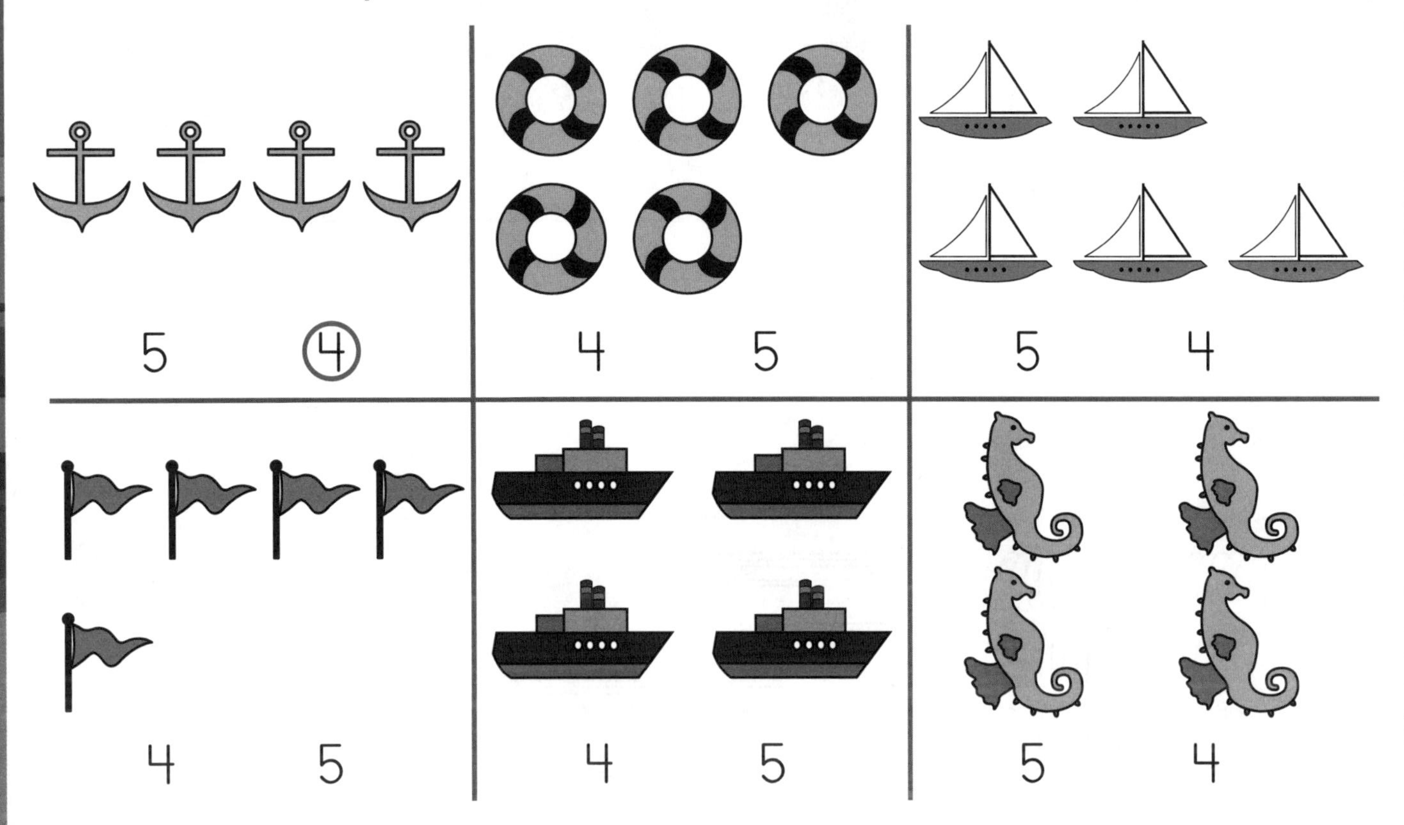

Write.

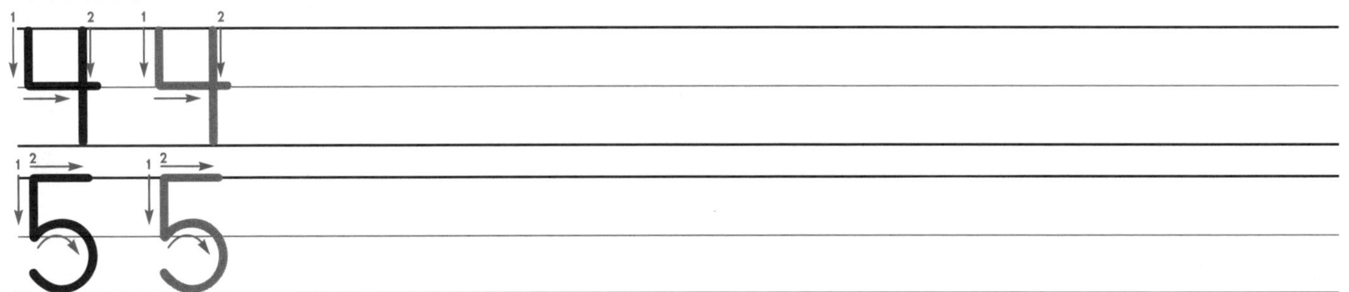

Write how many.

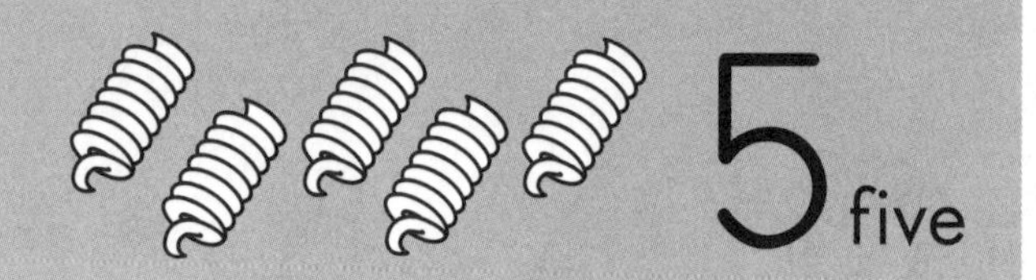

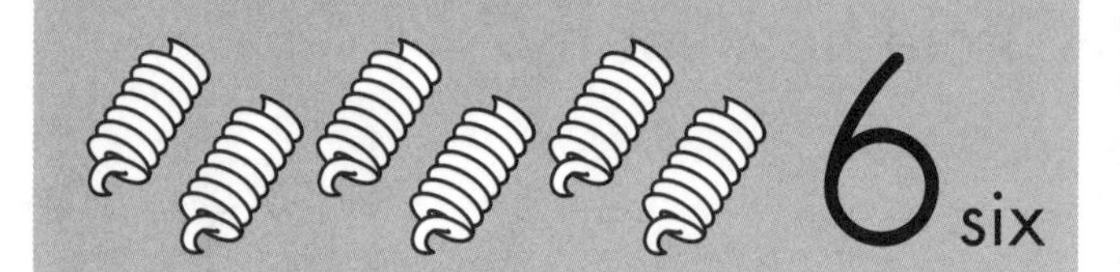

Color the groups with 6.

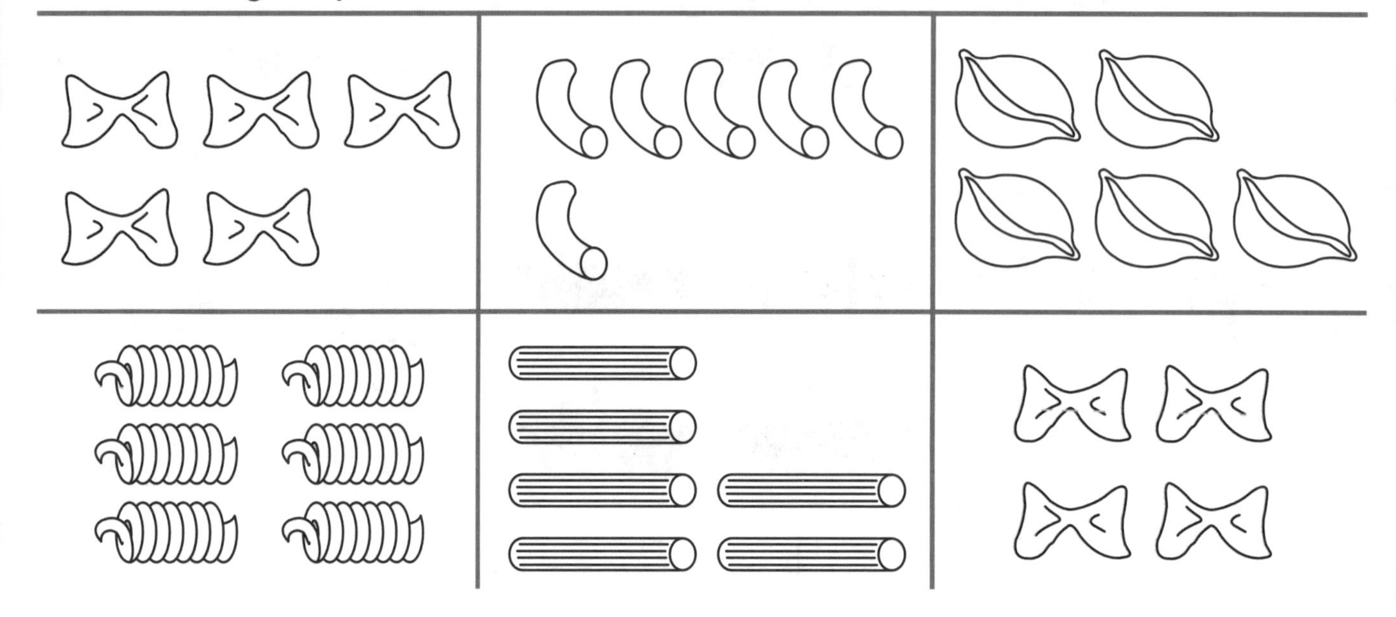

Draw windows to show how many.

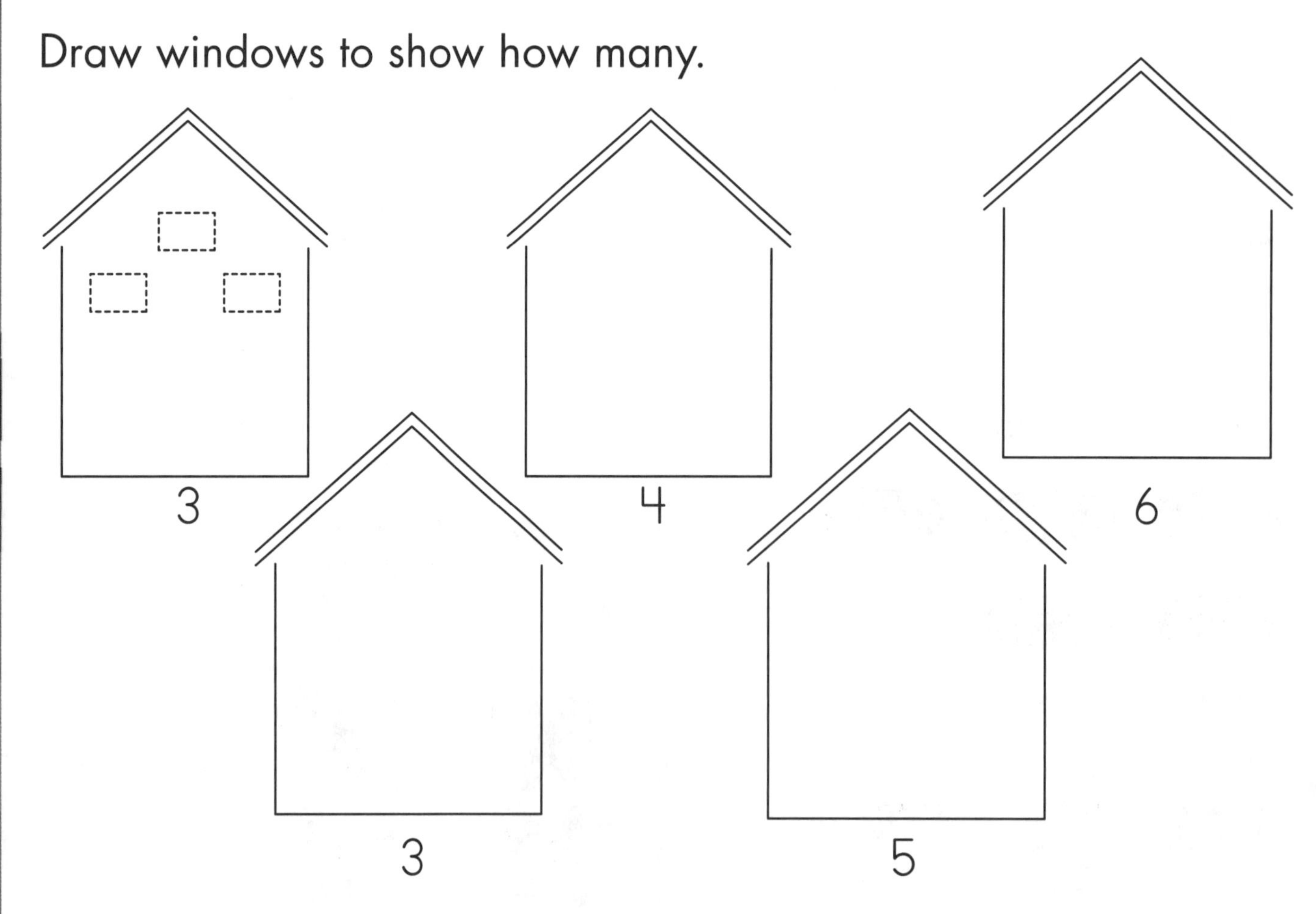

Circle how many.

5 6

5 6

5 6

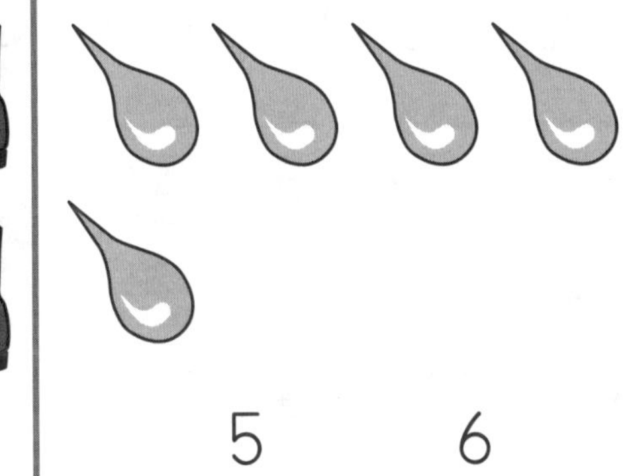

5 6

5 6

5 6

Write.

Write how many.

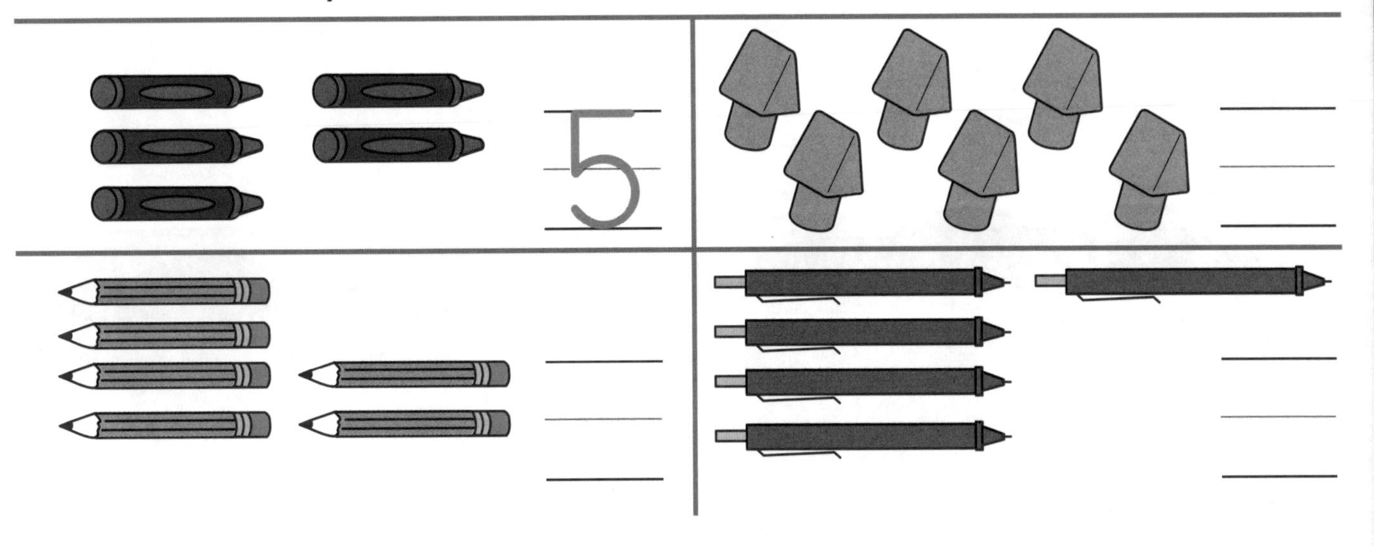

Circle the groups with 7.

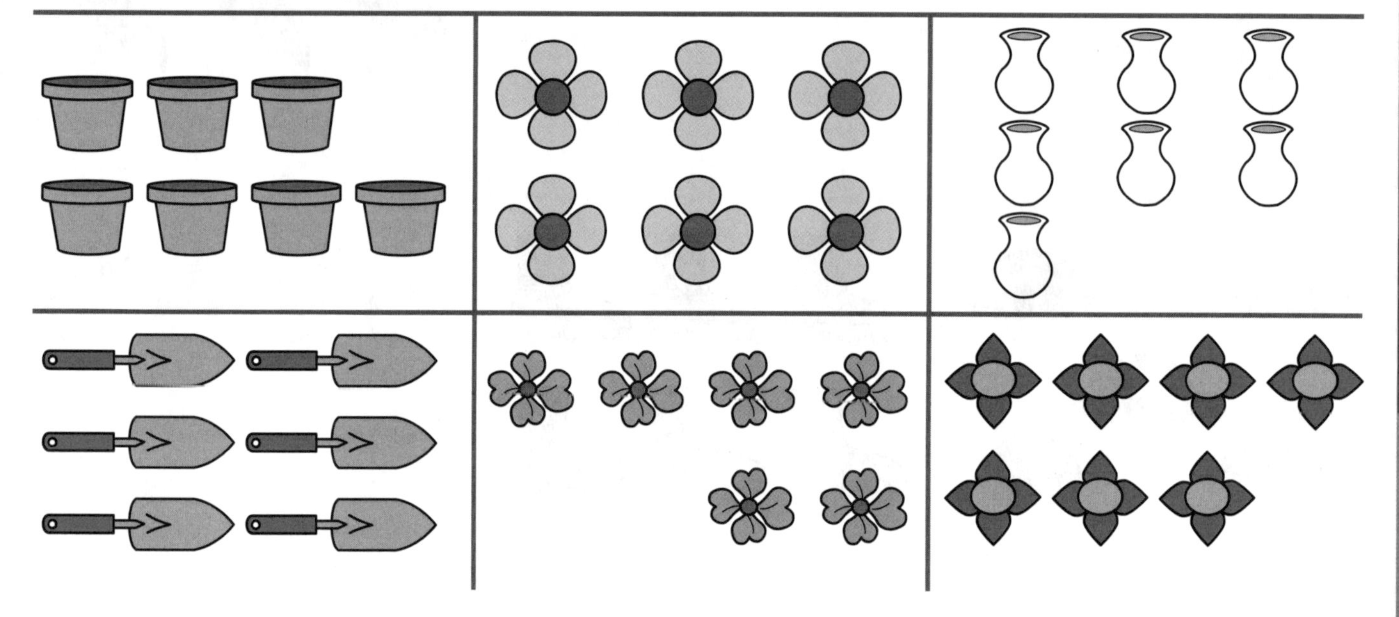

Draw flowers to show how many.

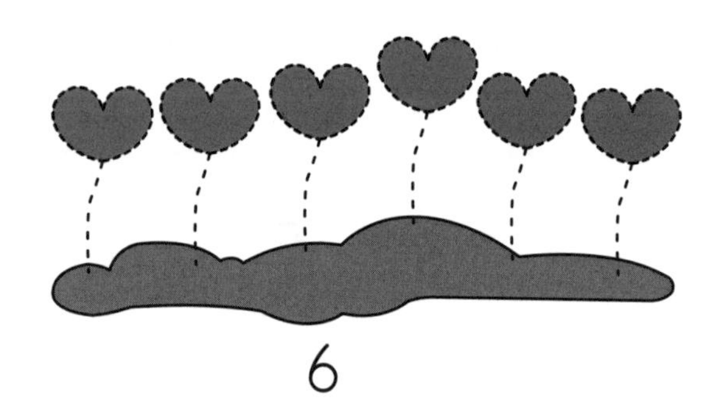

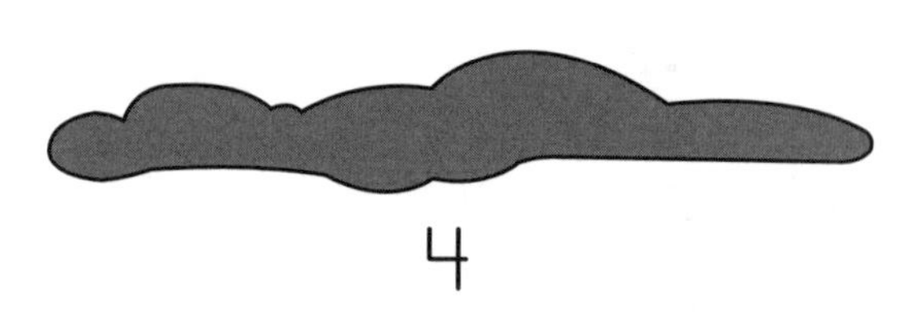

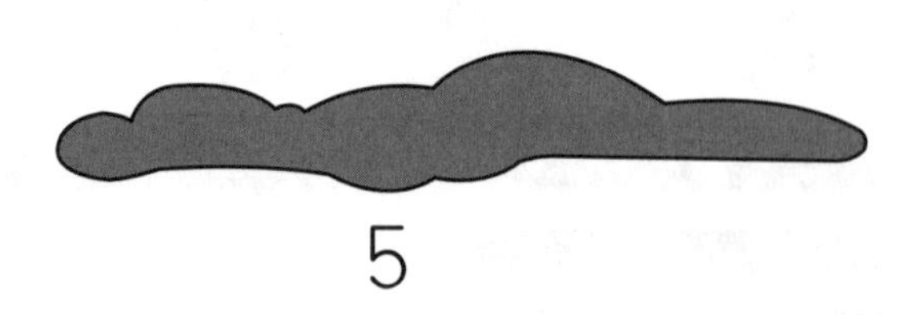

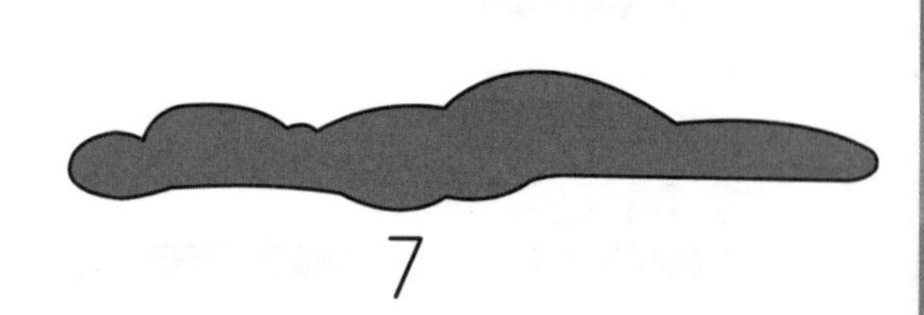

Circle how many.

6 7

6 7

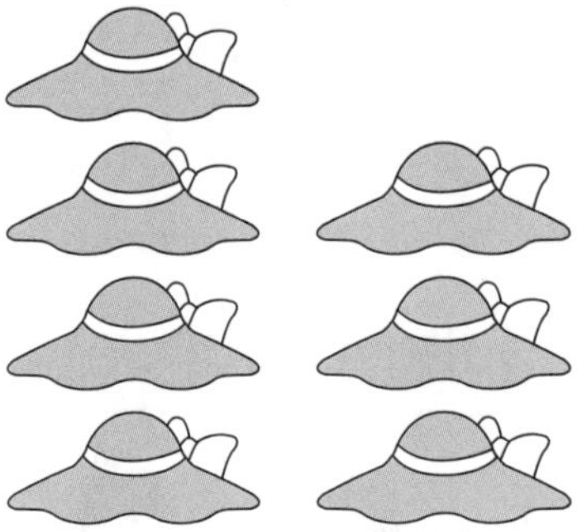

6 7

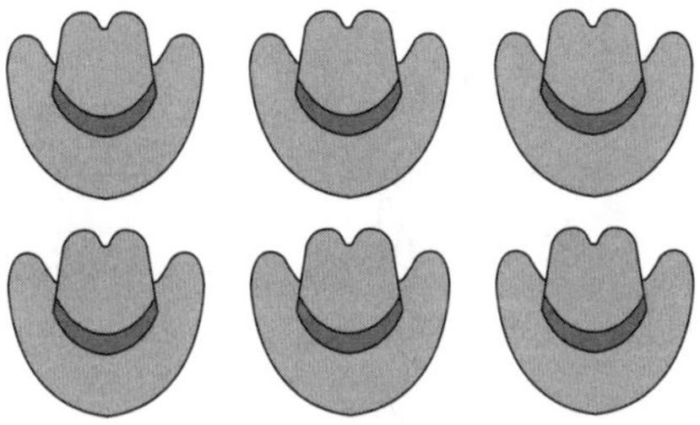

6 7

6 7

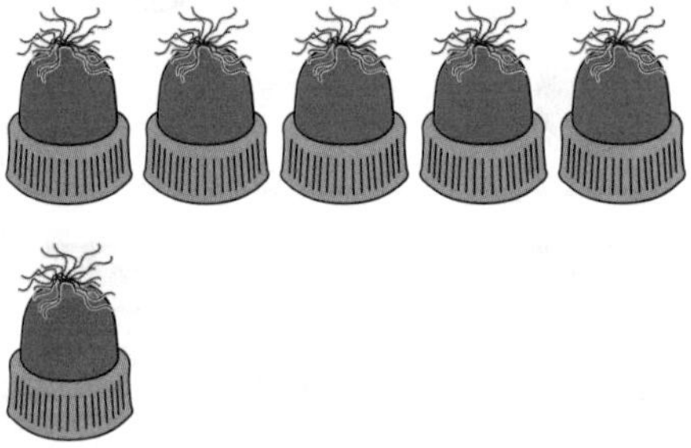

6 7

Write.

6 6

7 7

Write how many.

6

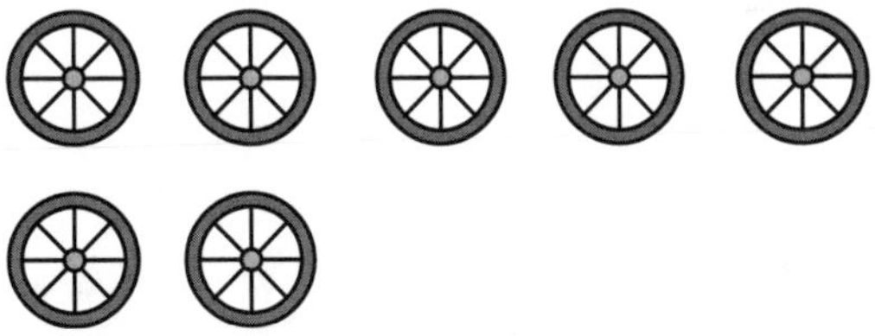

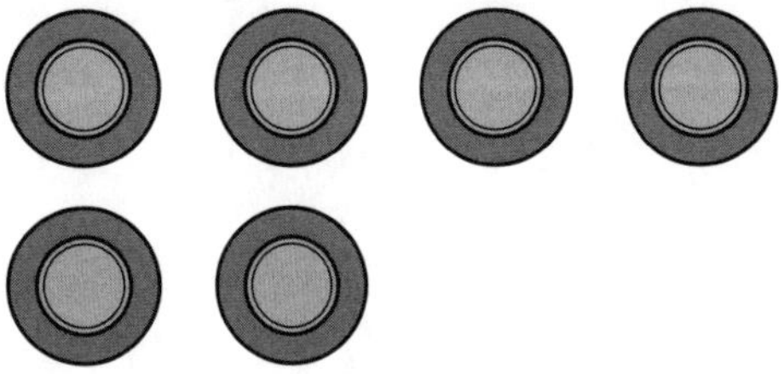

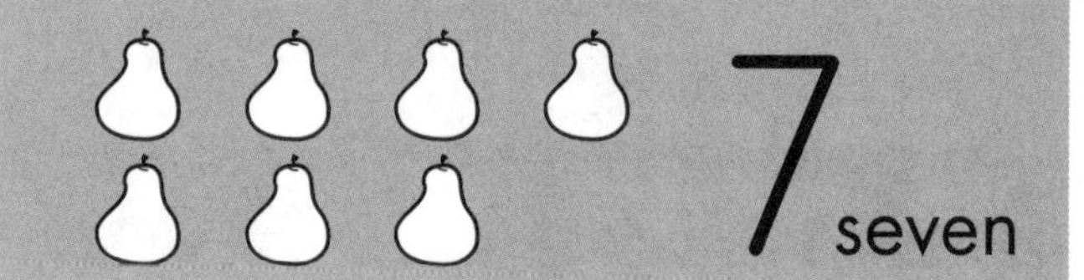

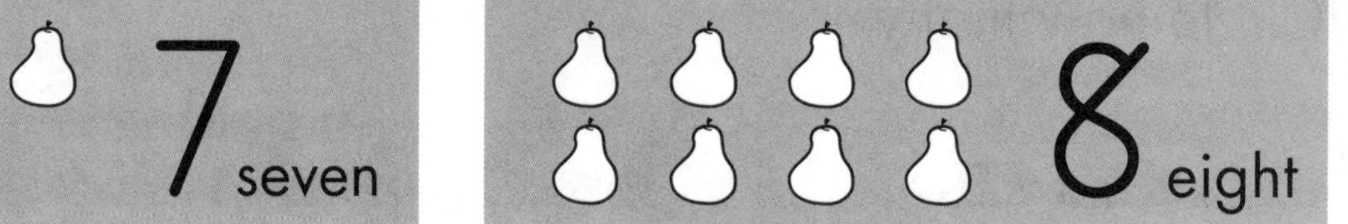

Circle the groups with 8.

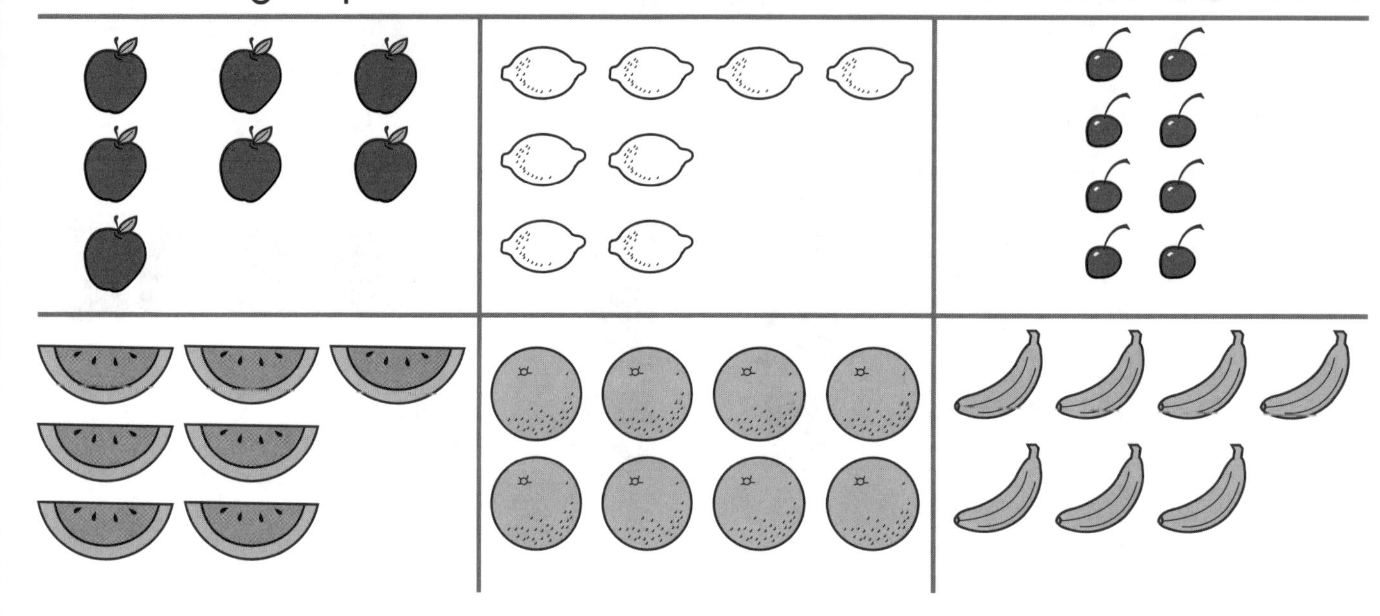

Draw cherries to show how many.

Circle how many.

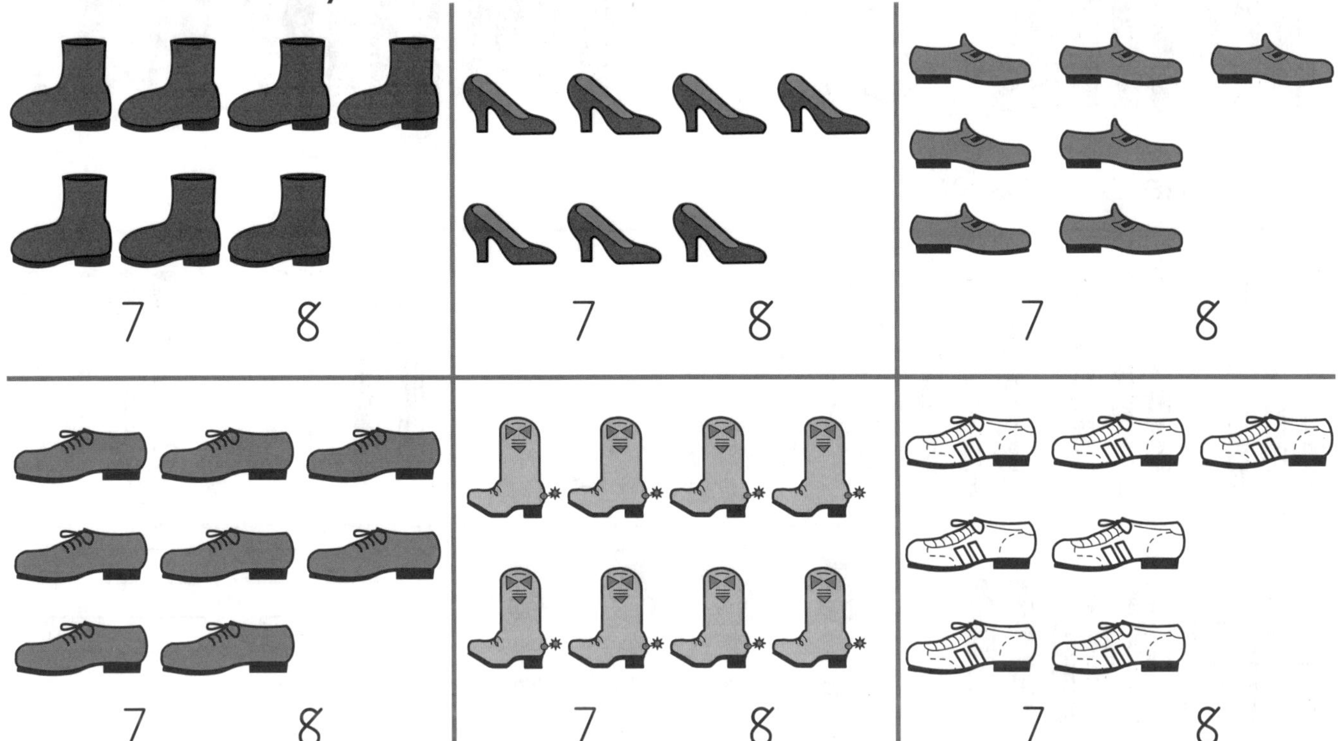

Write.

7 7

8 8

Write how many.

8 eight

9 nine

Circle the groups with 9.

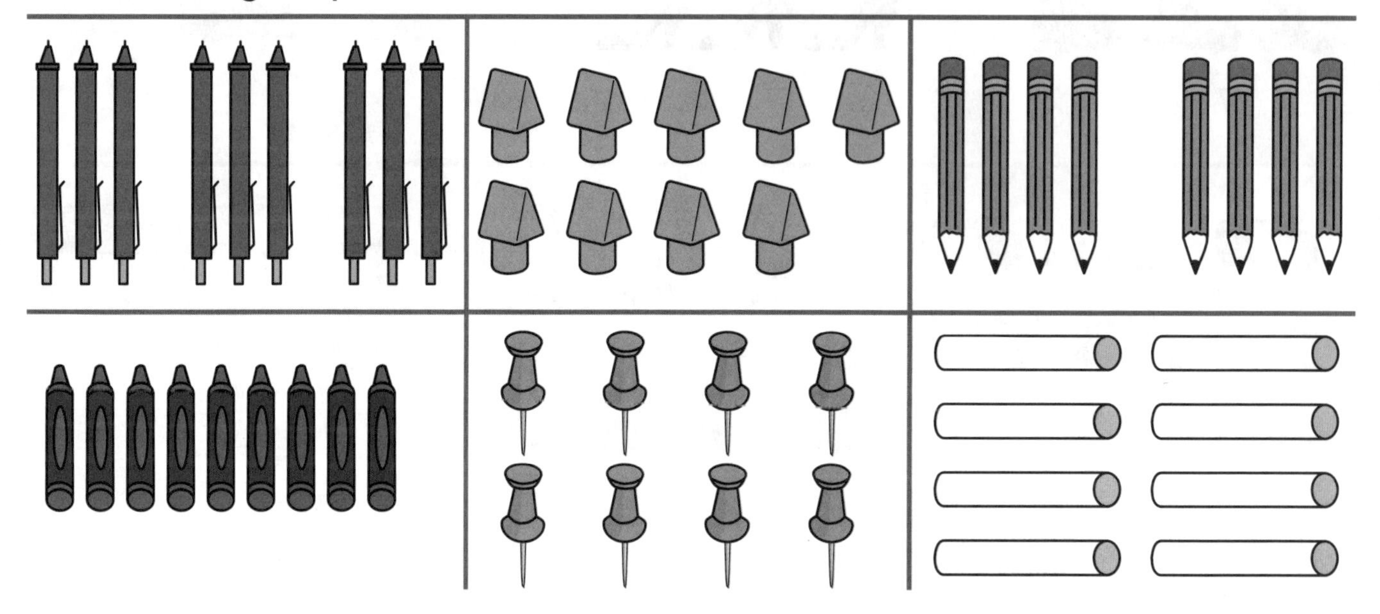

Draw beads to show how many.

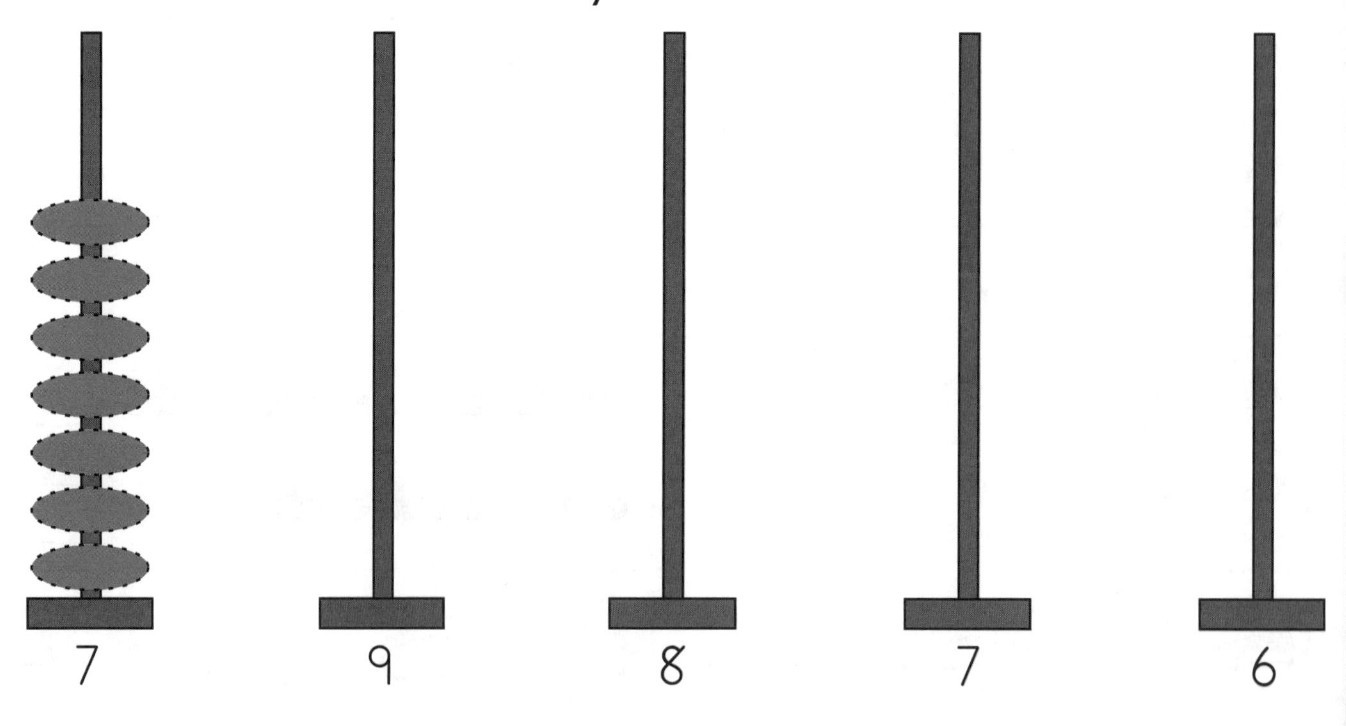

Circle how many.

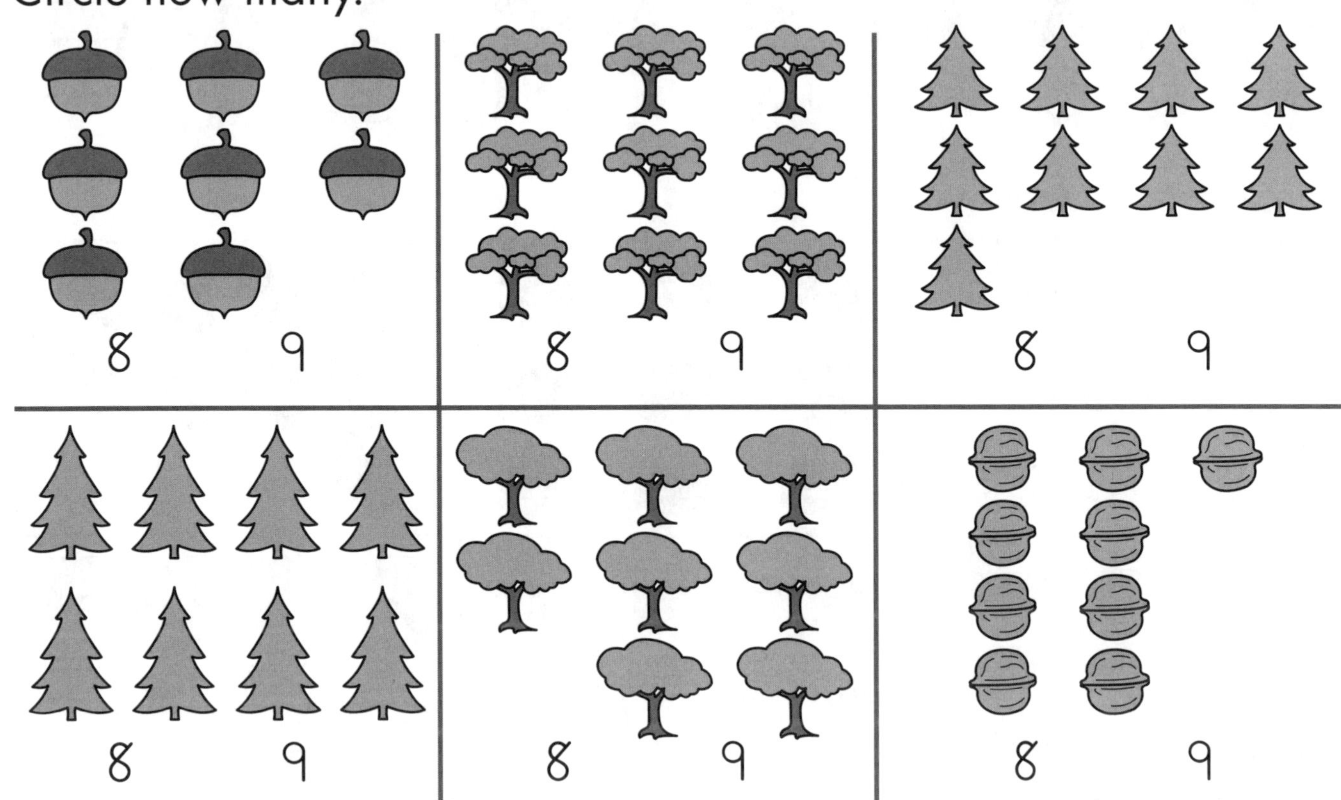

Write.

Write how many.

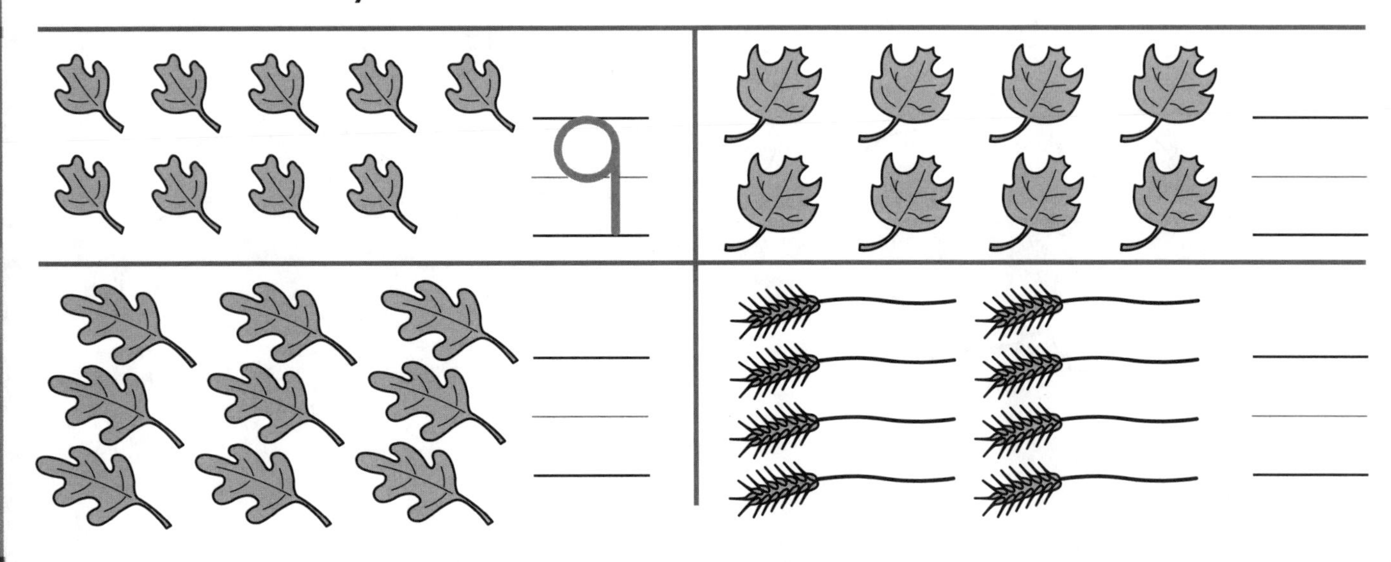

9 nine

10 ten

Circle the groups with 10.

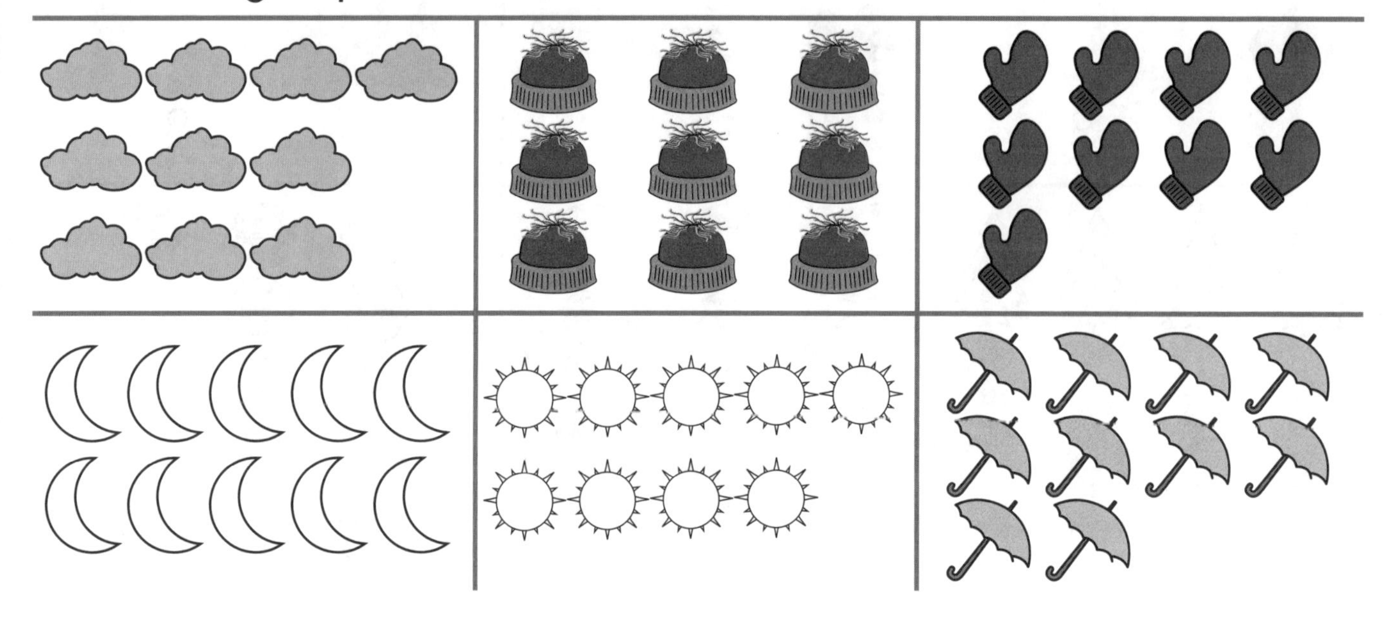

Draw raindrops to show how many.

Circle how many.

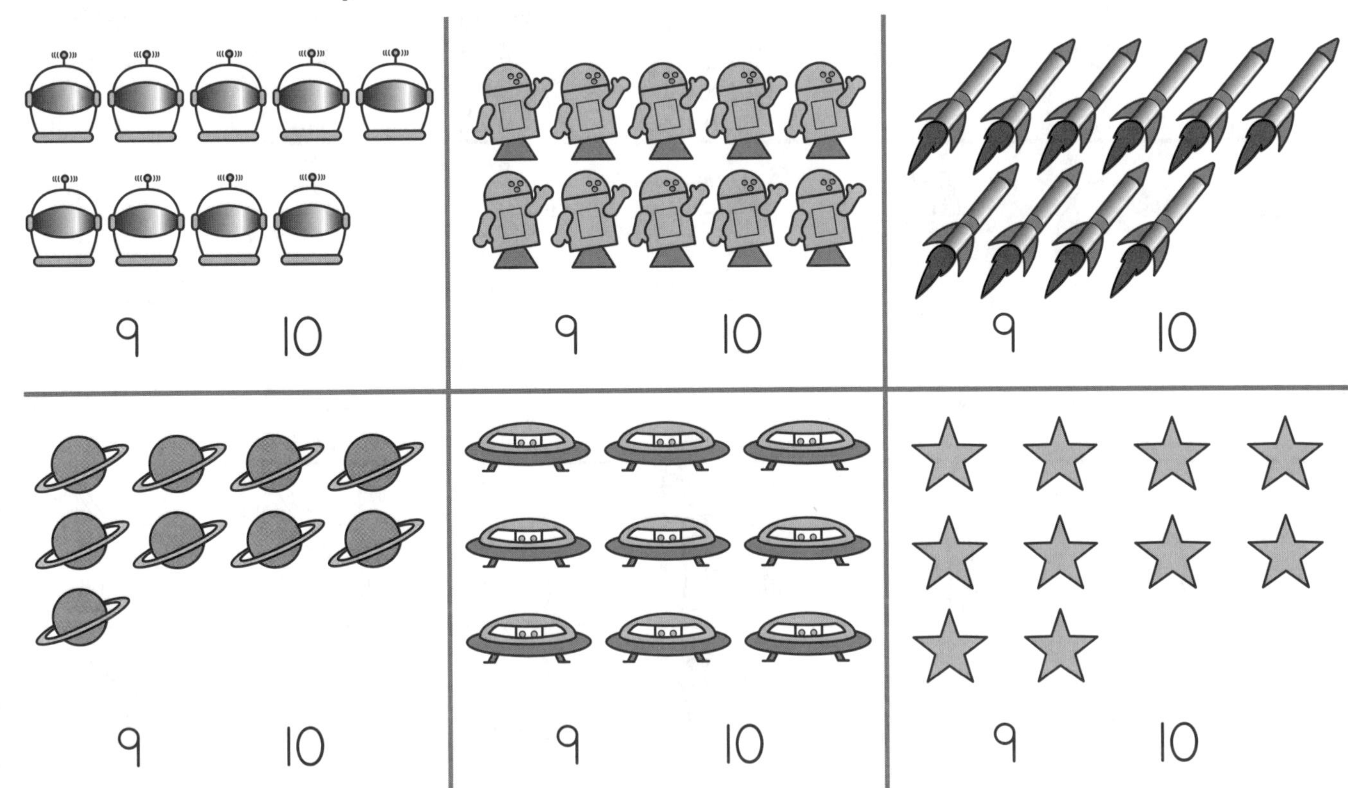

Write.

Write how many.

Color the one named.

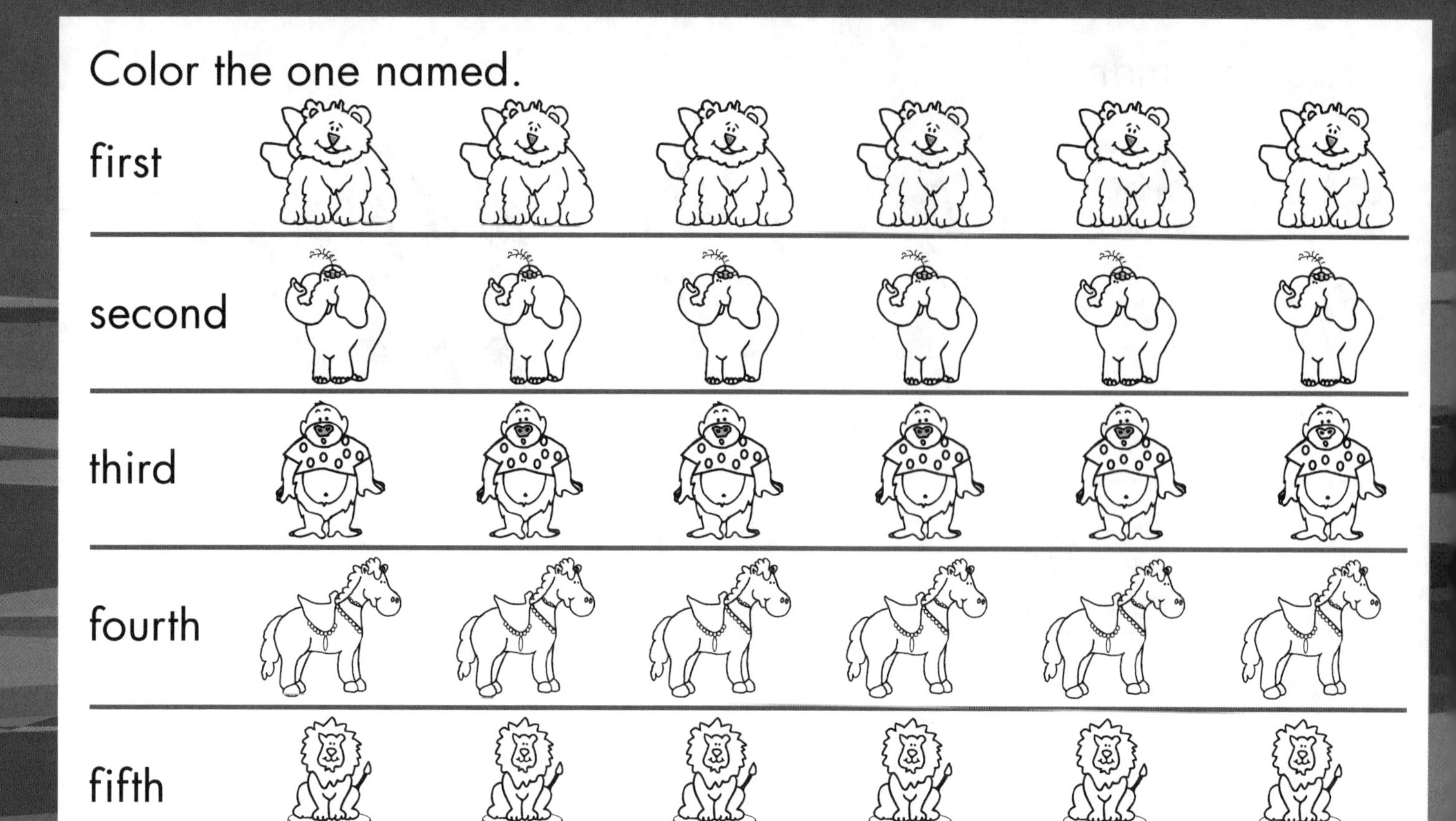

Start at 10 and count backward to connect the dots.

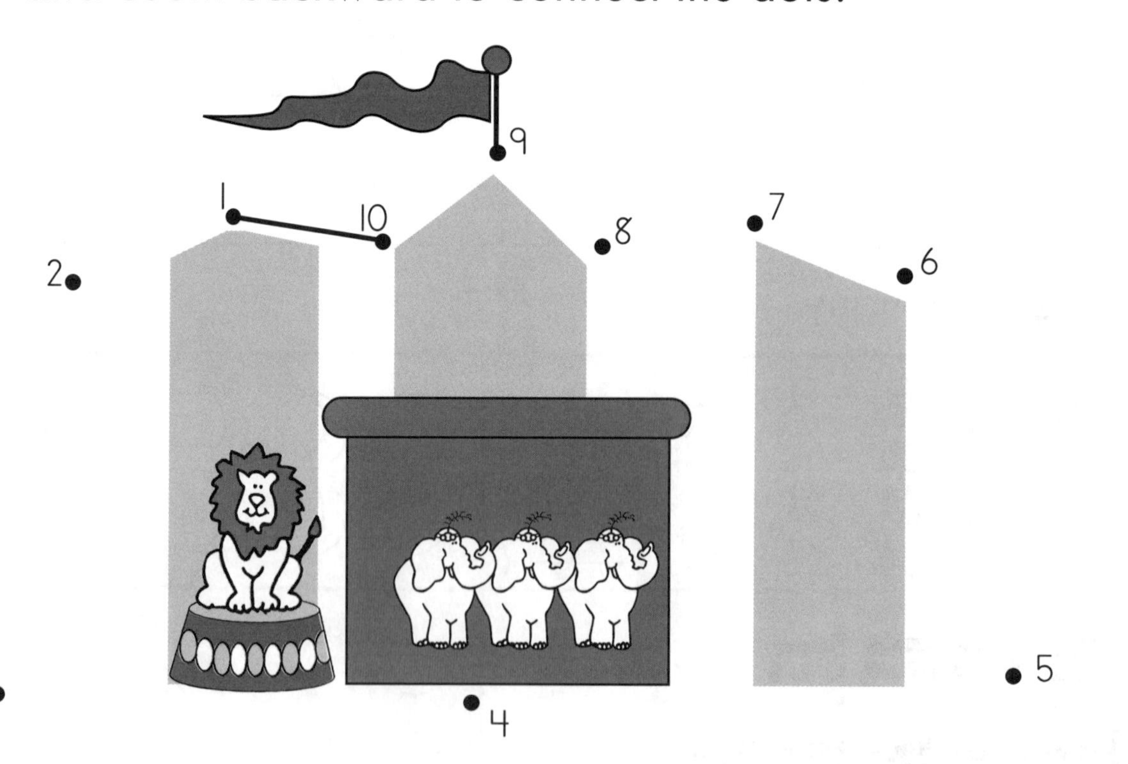

11 eleven

12 twelve

Count to the number. Mark as you count.

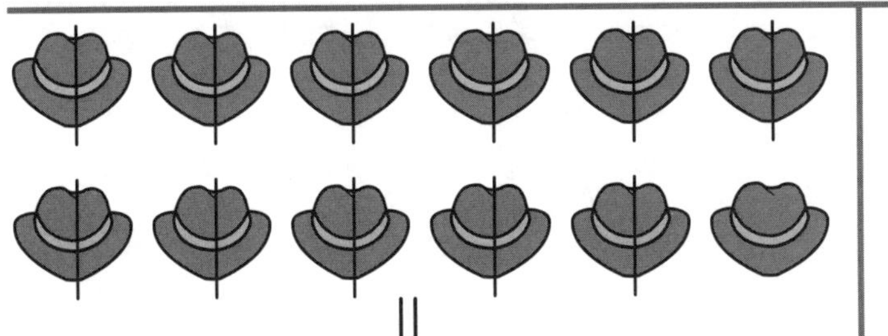

11

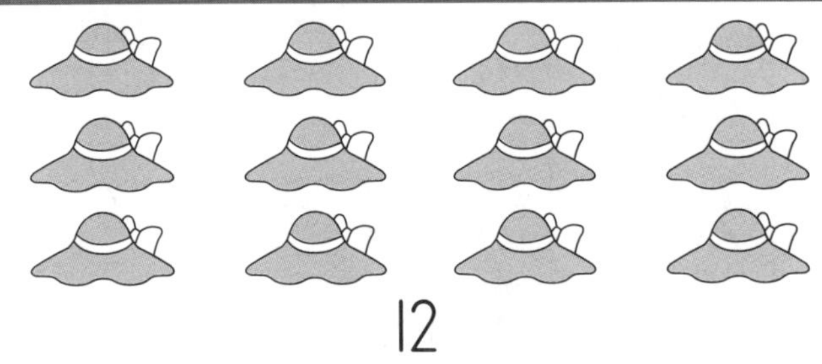

12

12

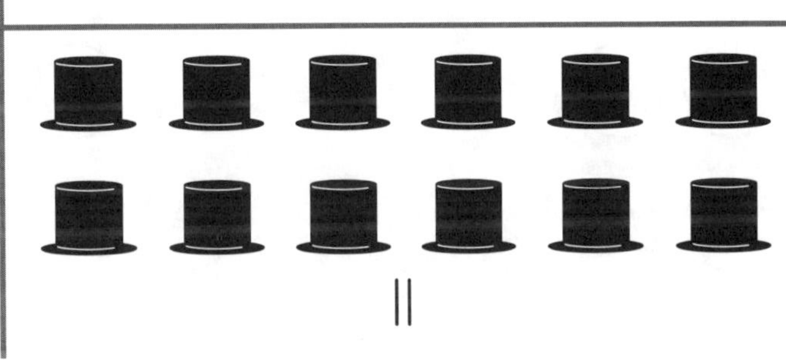

11

Write how many.

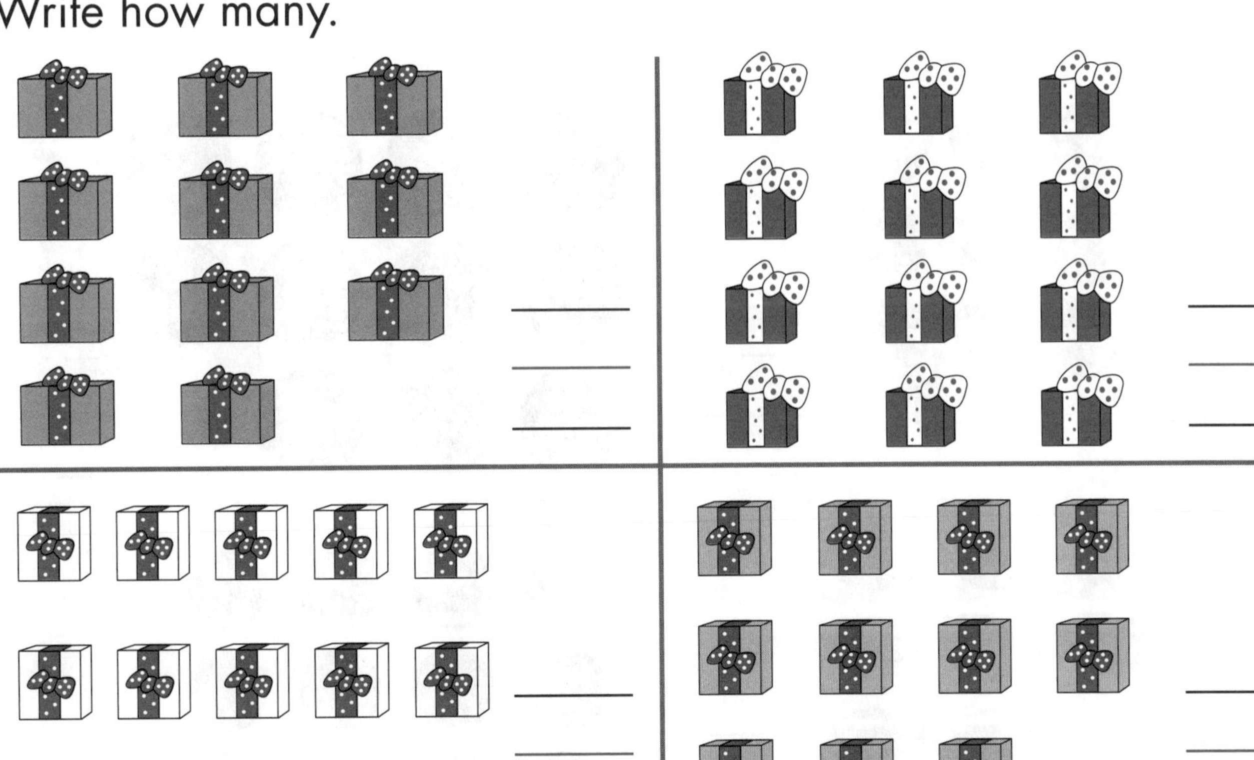

13

14

Count to the number.

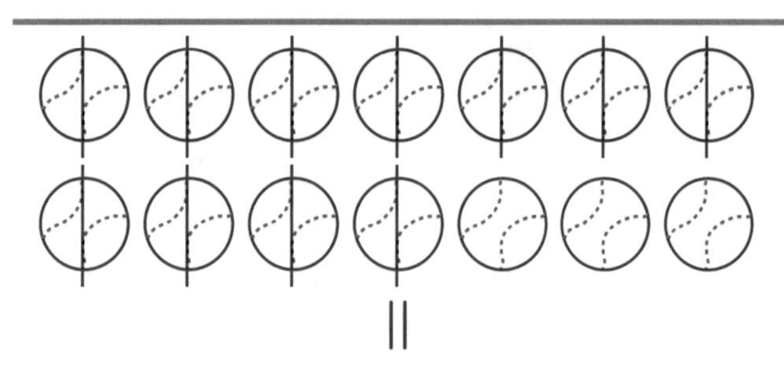

11

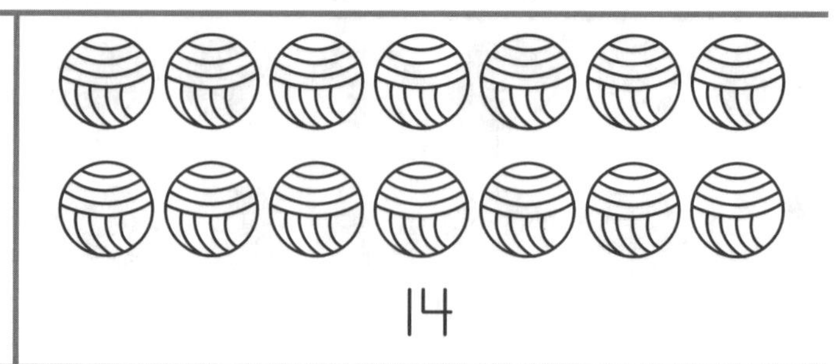

14

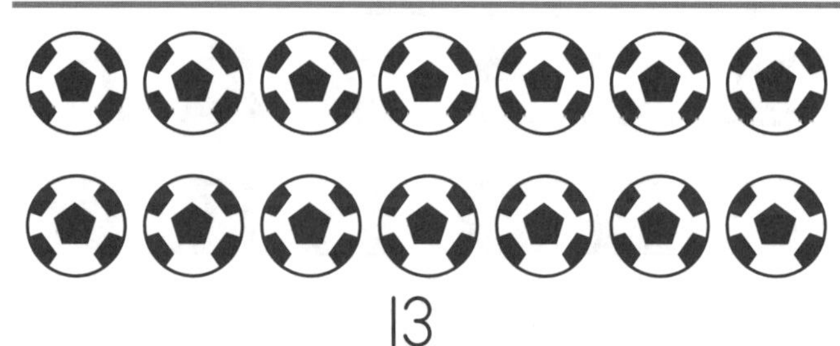

13

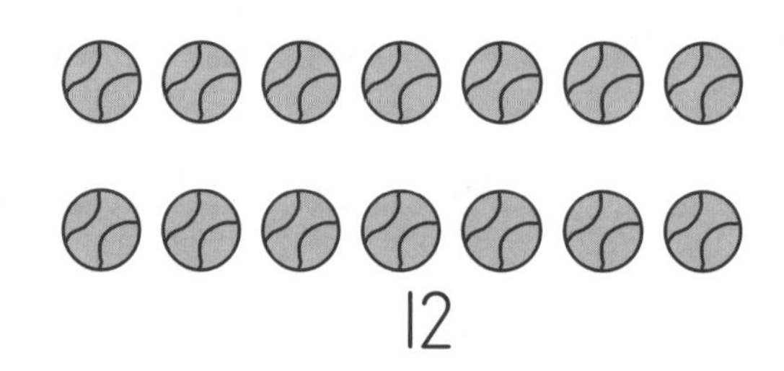

12

Write how many.

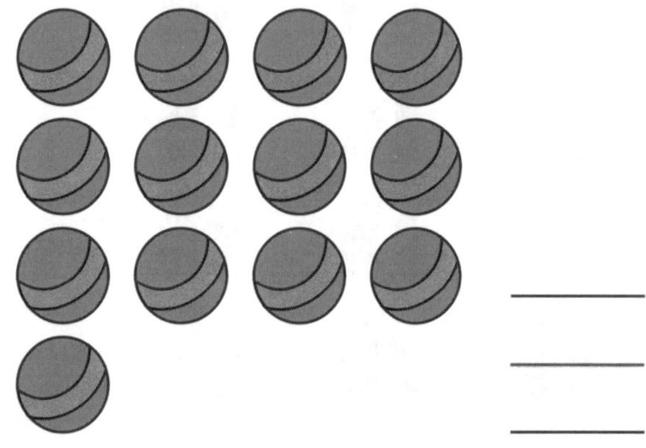

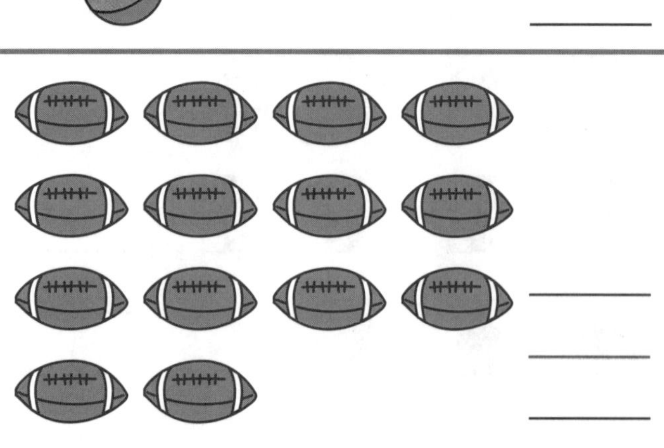

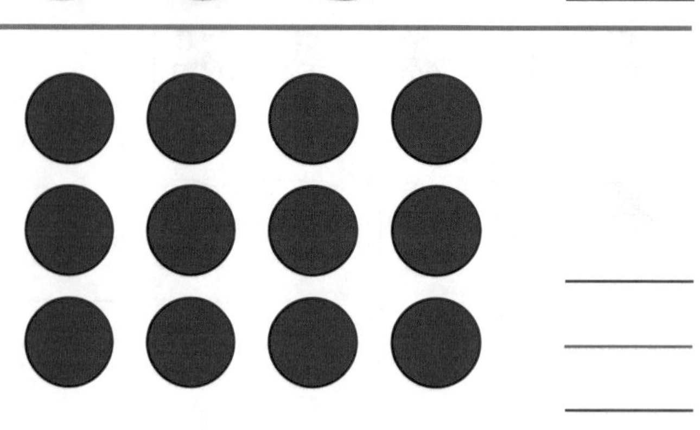

15 16

Count to the number.

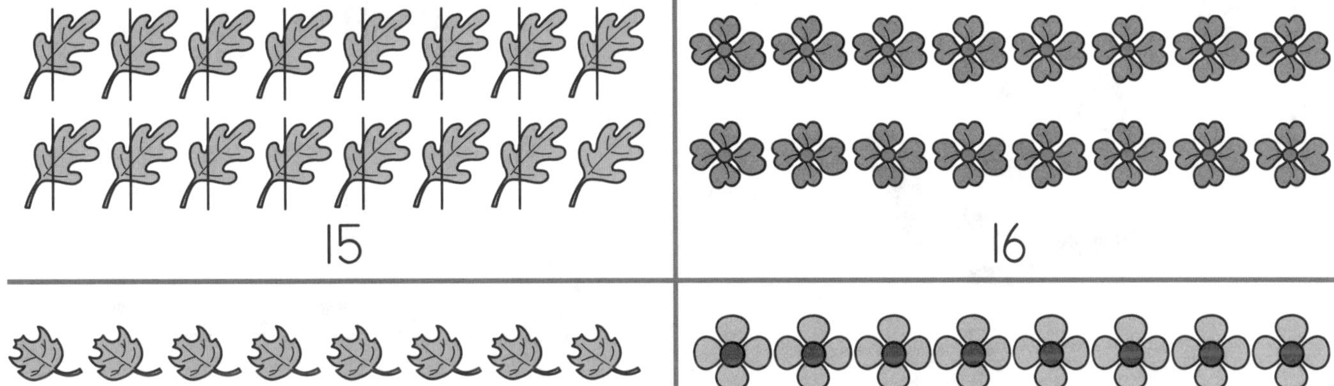

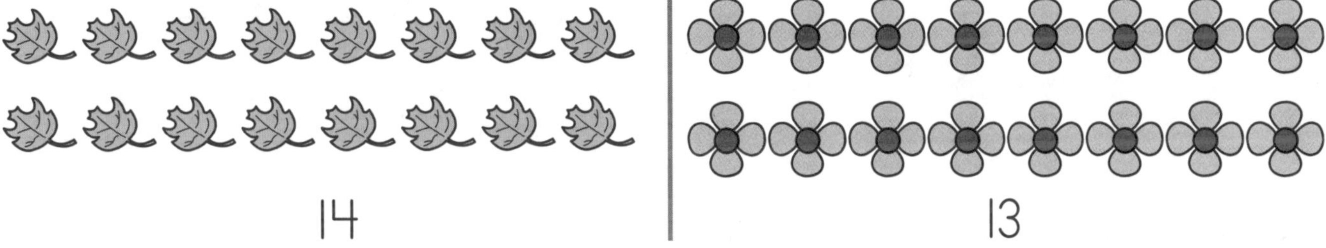

Write how many.

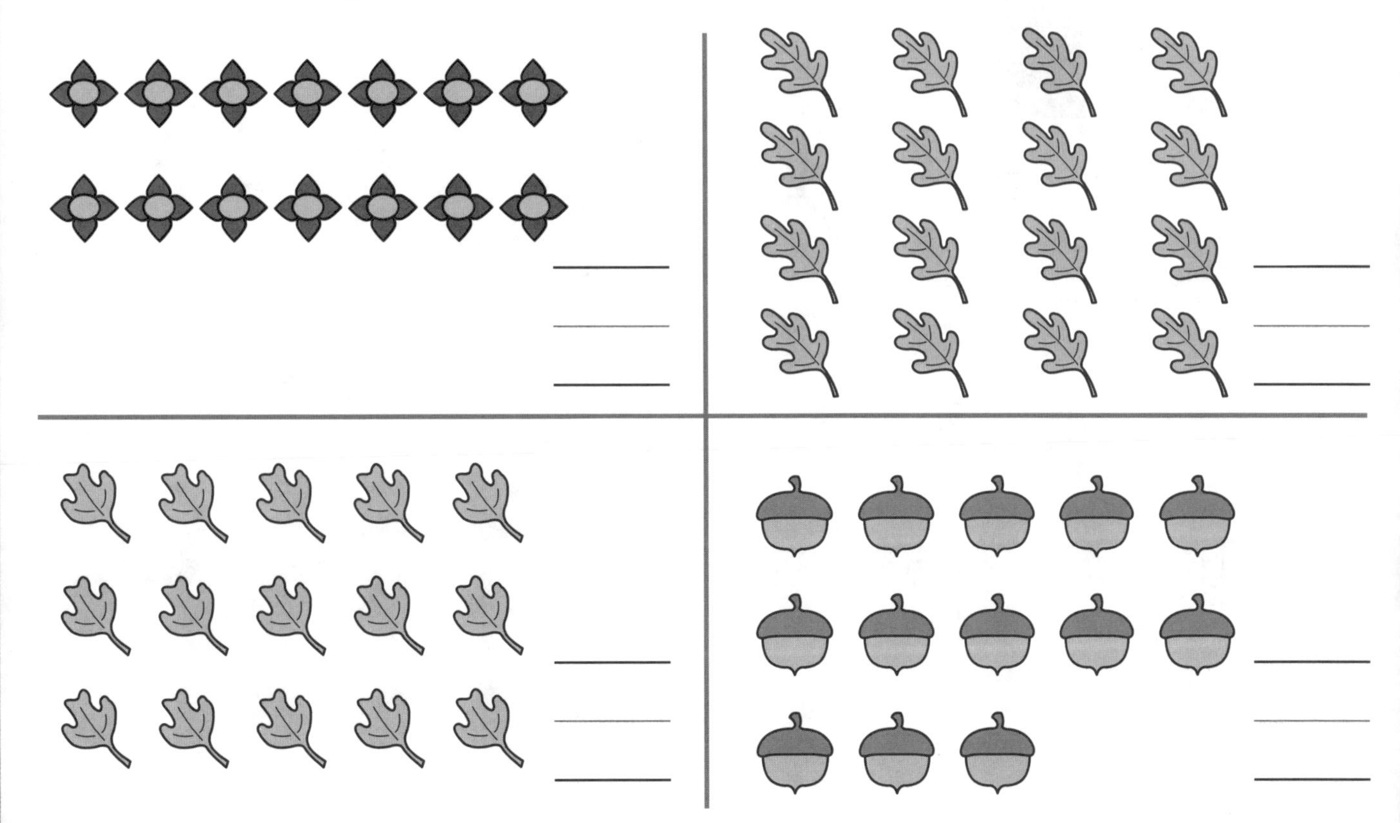

Start at 1 and connect the dots.
Find the number "just after" to connect.

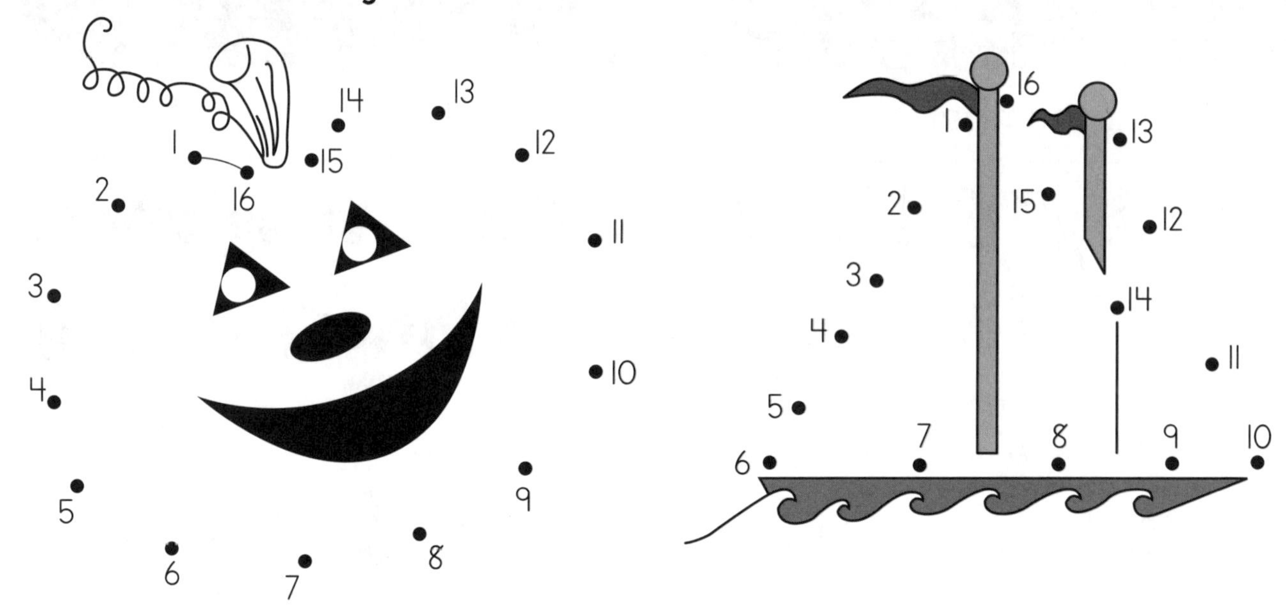

Start at 16 and connect the dots backward.
Find the number "just before" to connect

Count to the number.

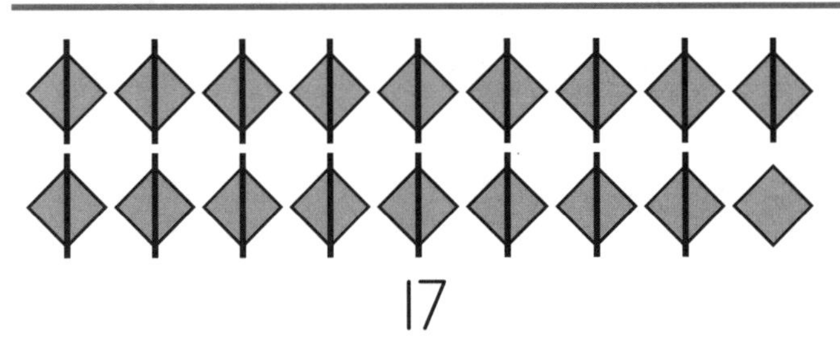

17

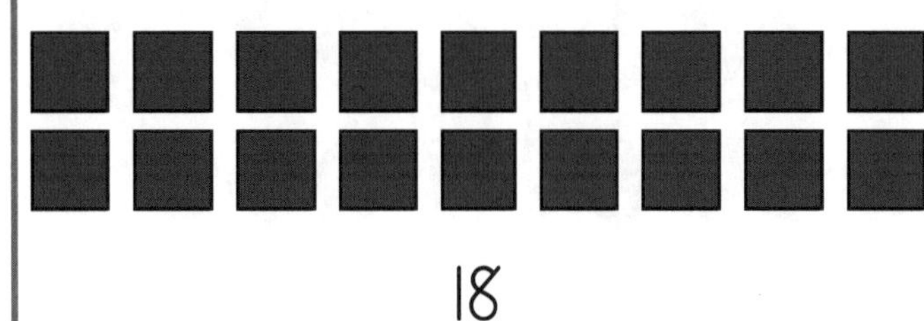

18

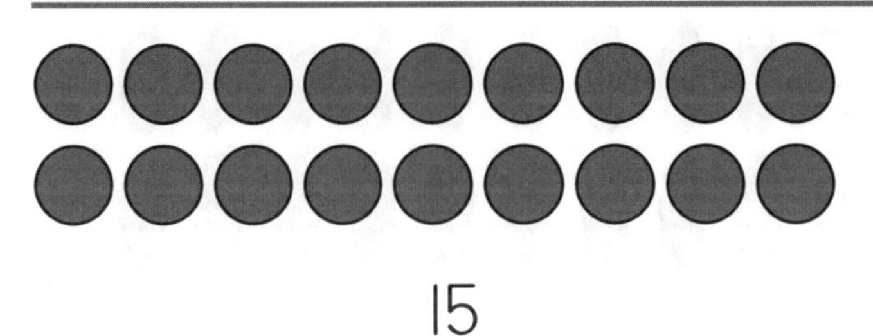

15

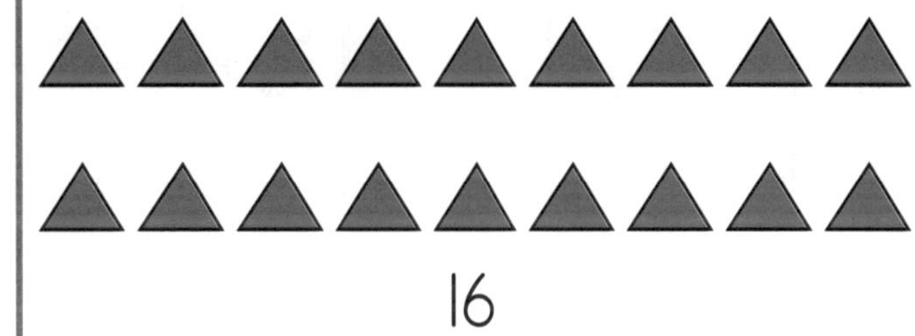

16

Write how many.

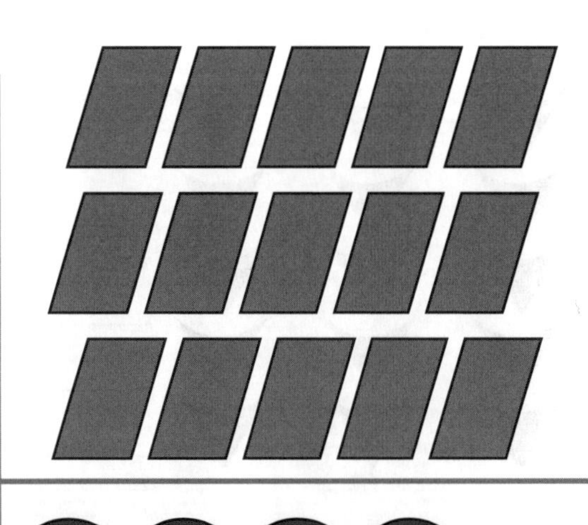

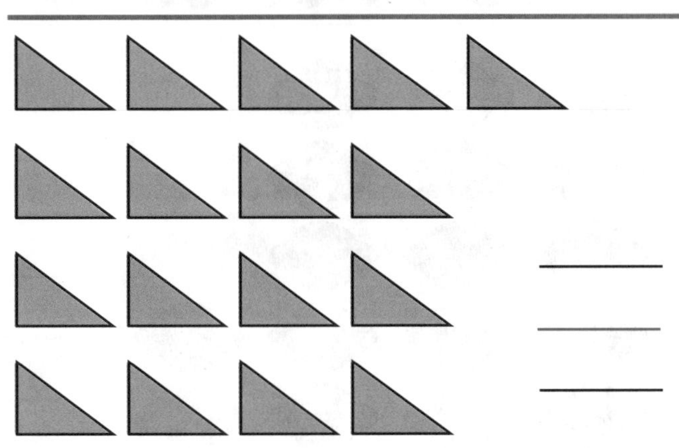

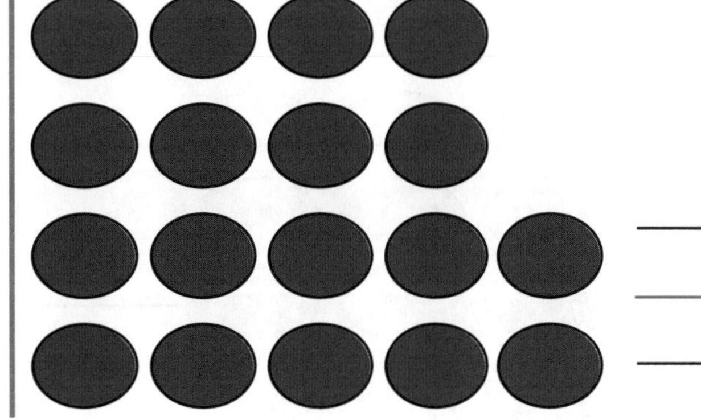

Count to the number.

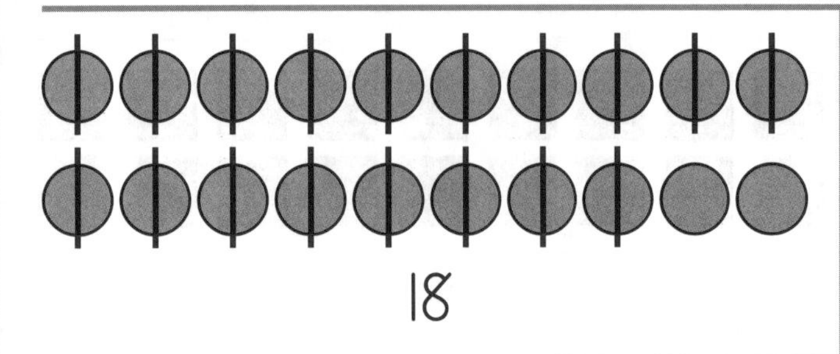

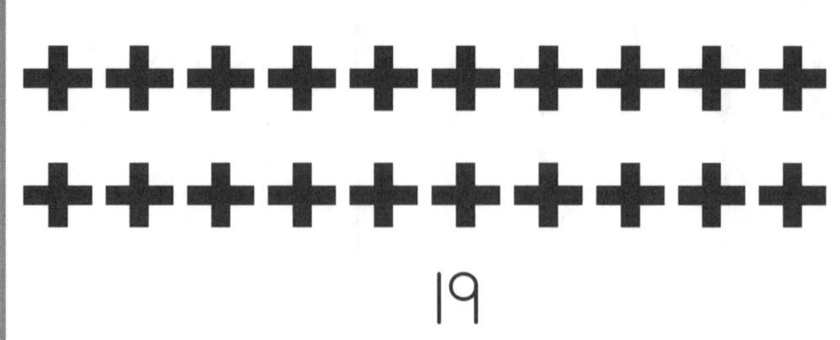

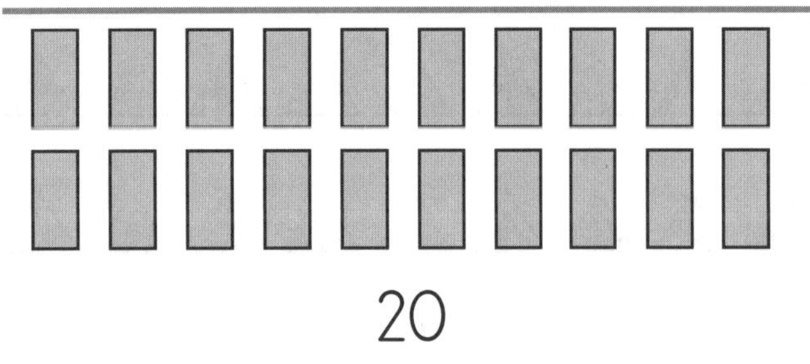

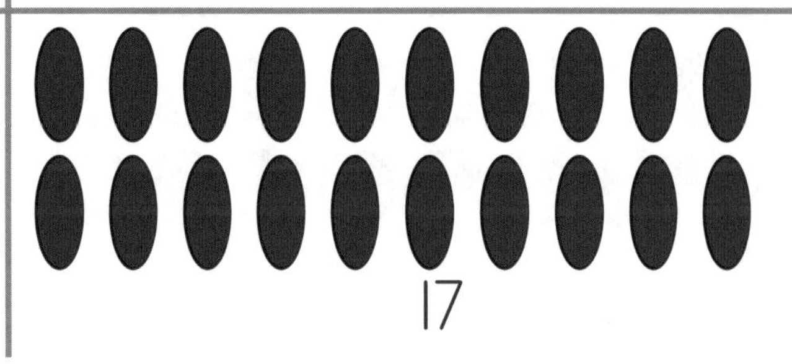

Write how many.

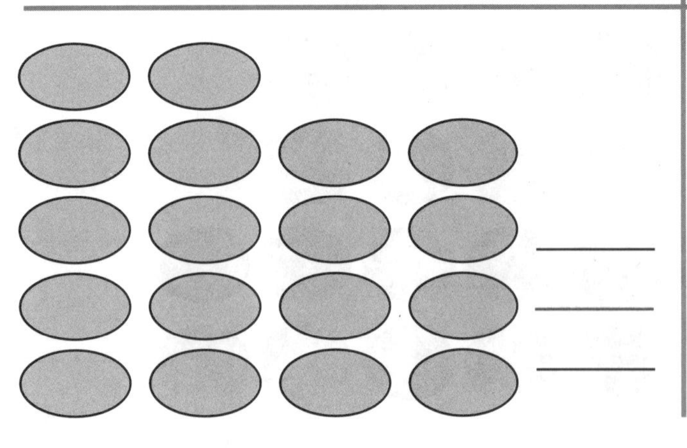

Count by twos.

Write the number that is "in between."

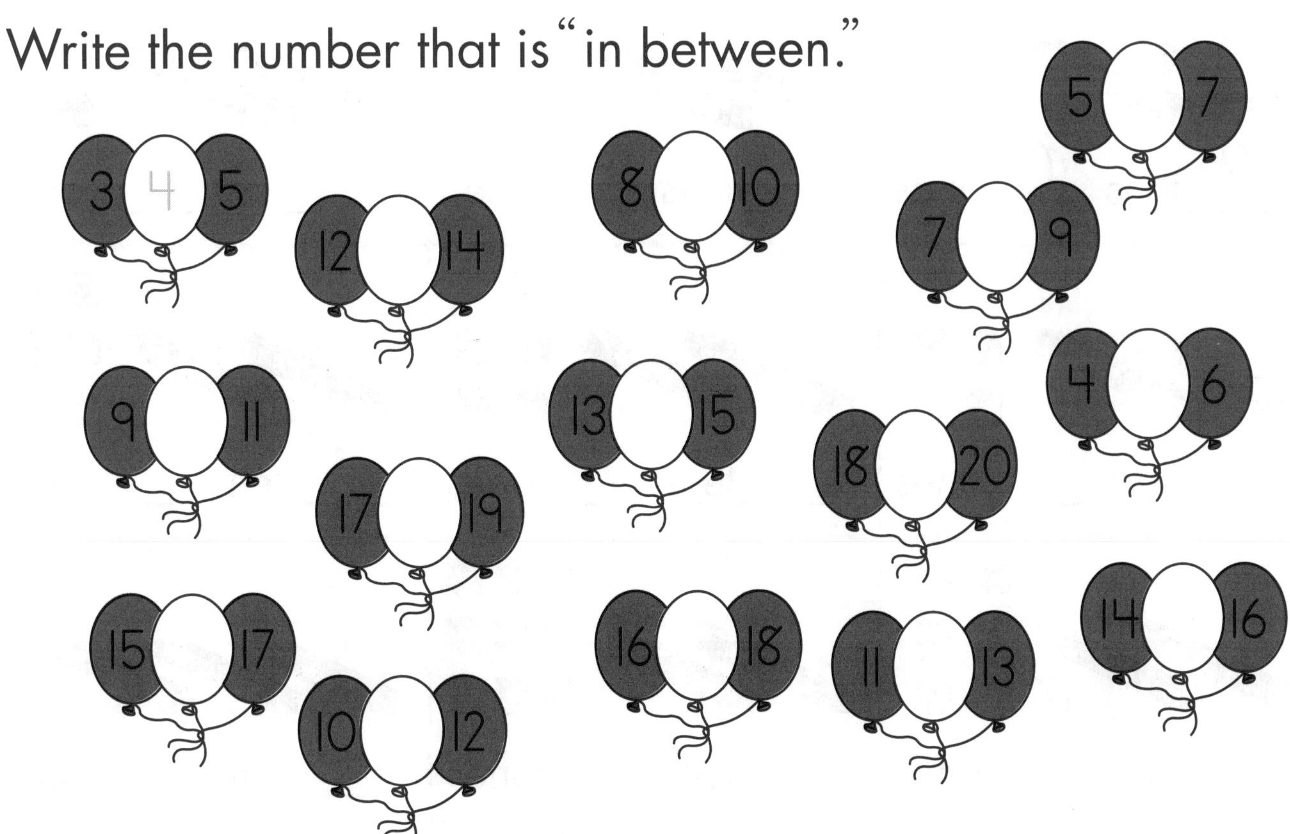

10 ones

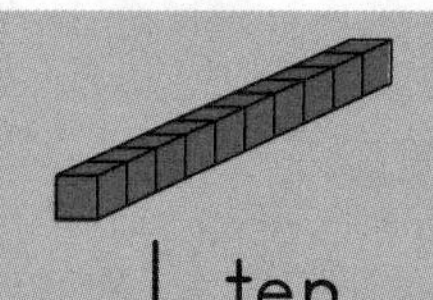

1 ten 0 ones

Write the number.

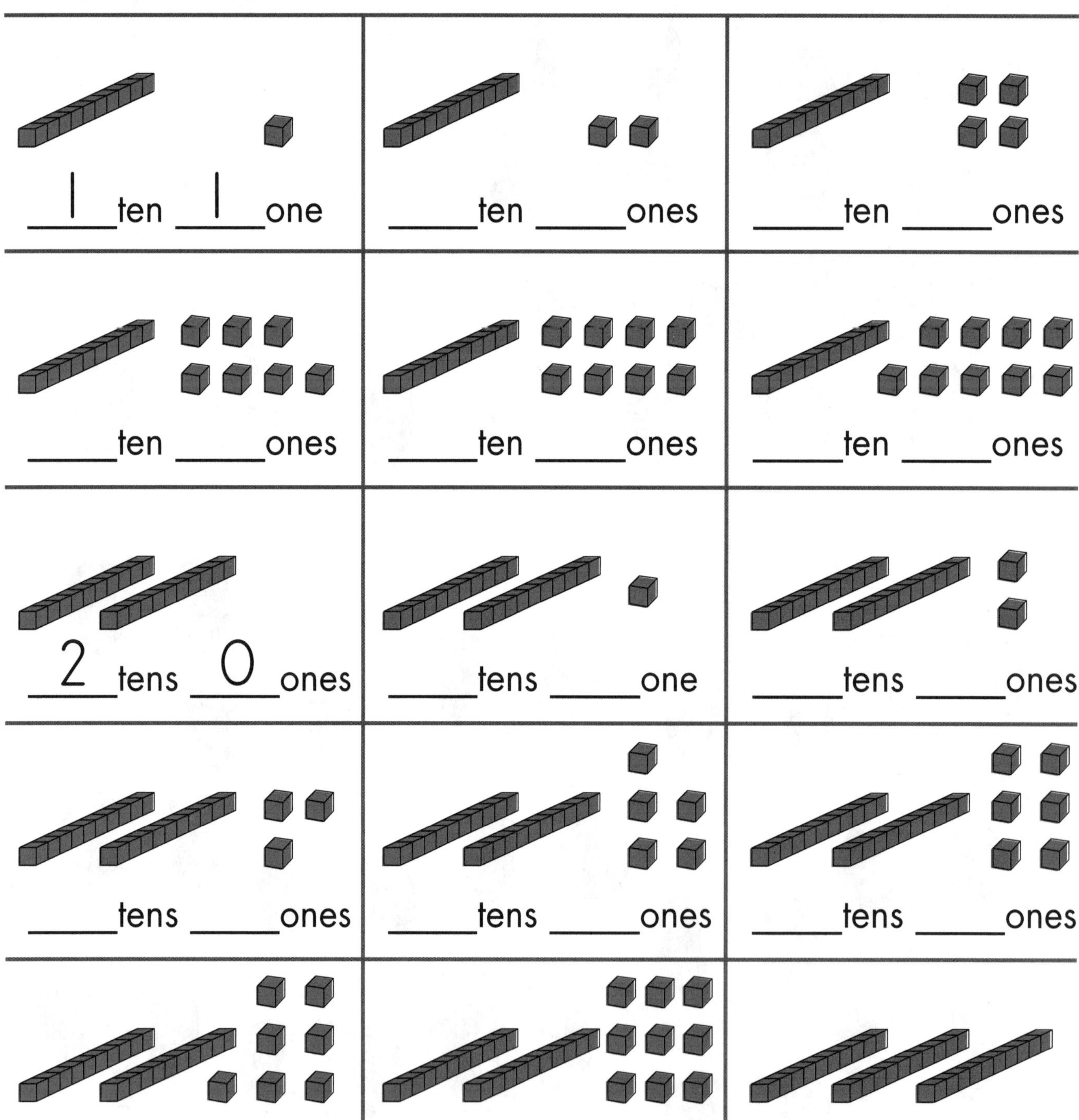

Write the number.

tens	ones
1	0

tens	ones

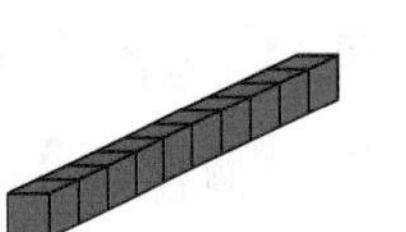

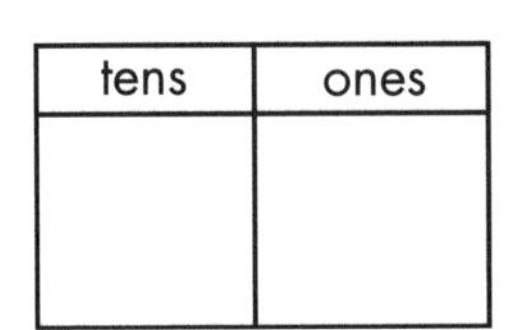

tens	ones

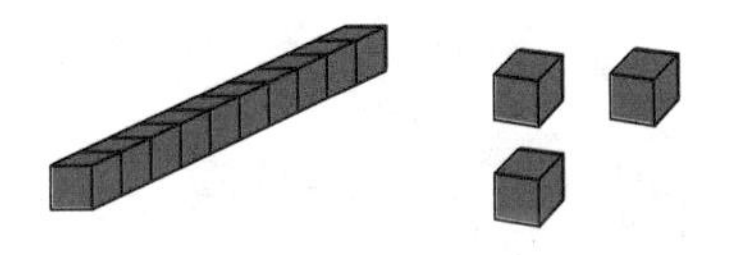

tens	ones

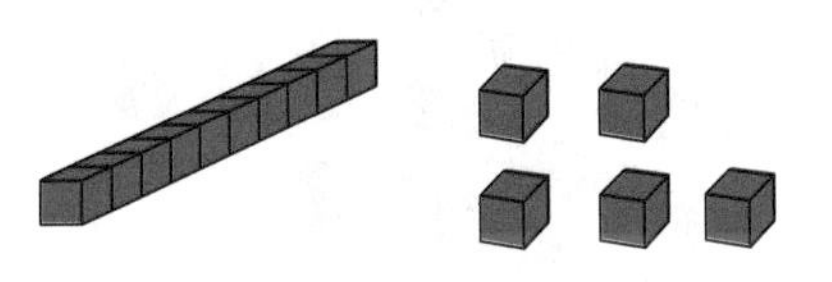

tens	ones

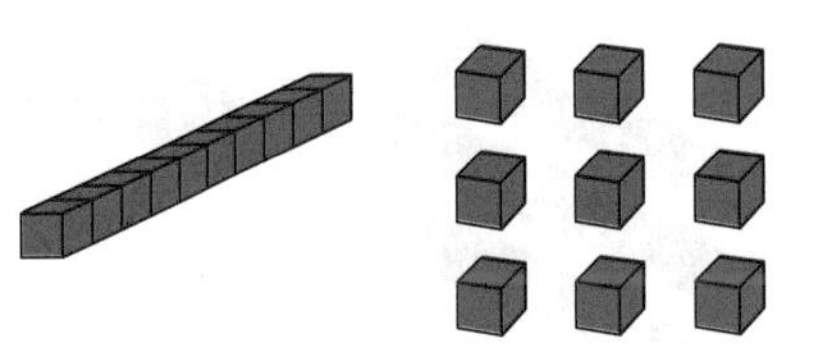

tens	ones

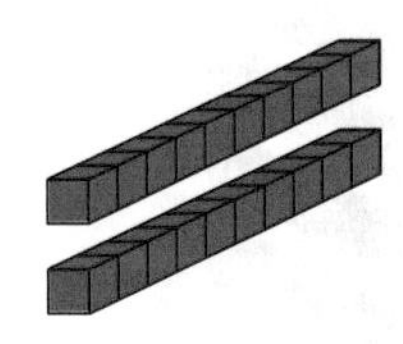

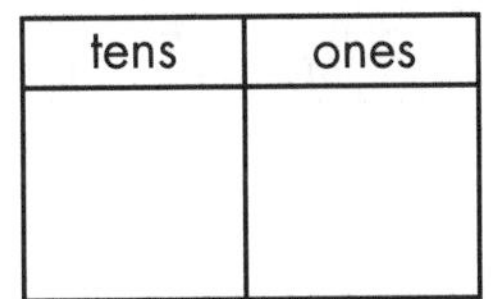

tens	ones

tens	ones

tens	ones

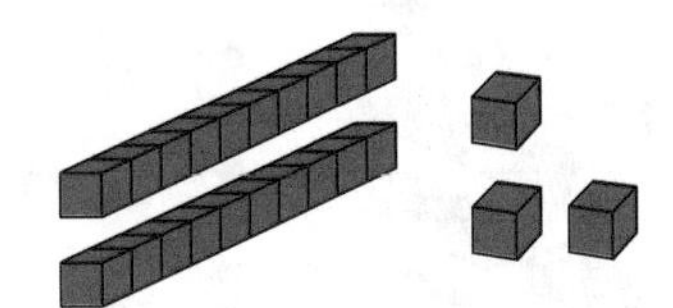

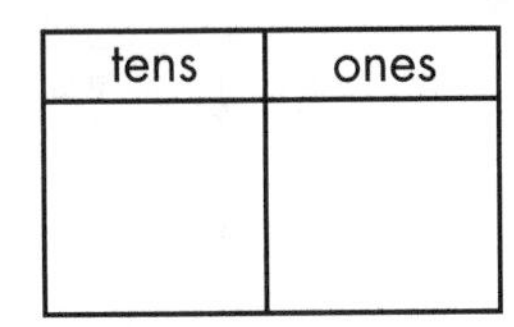

tens	ones

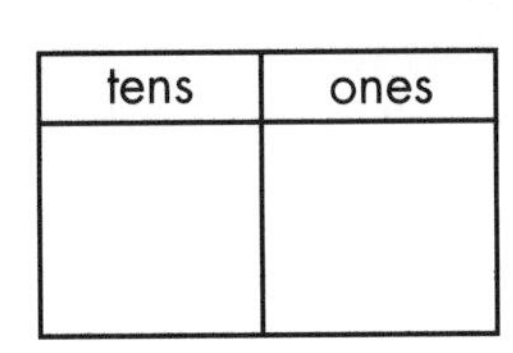

tens	ones

tens	ones

Write the number.

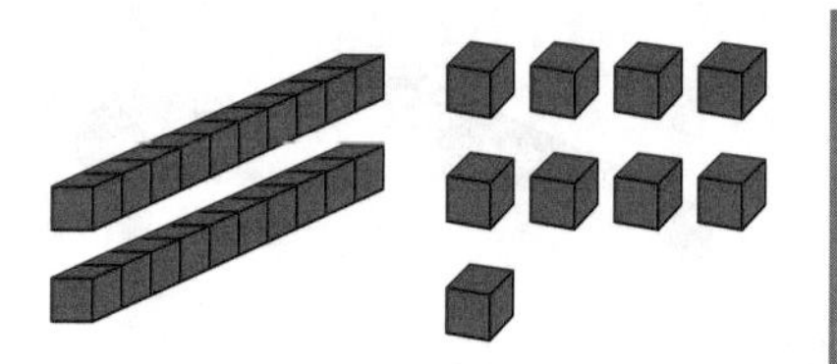

tens	ones
2	9

tens	ones

tens	ones

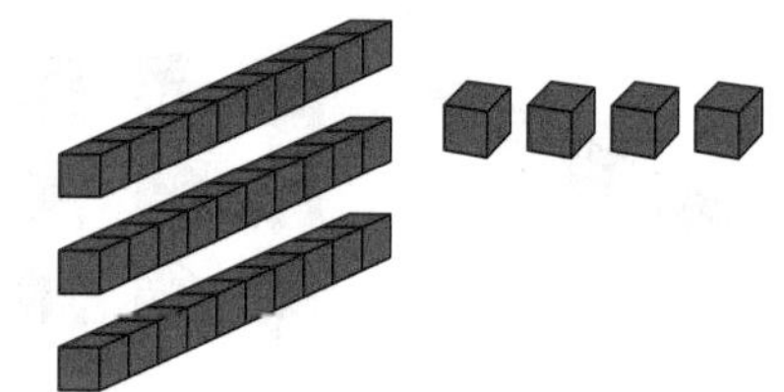

tens	ones

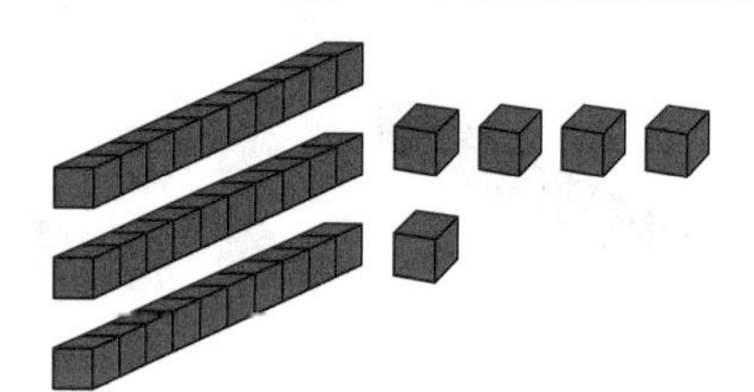

tens	ones

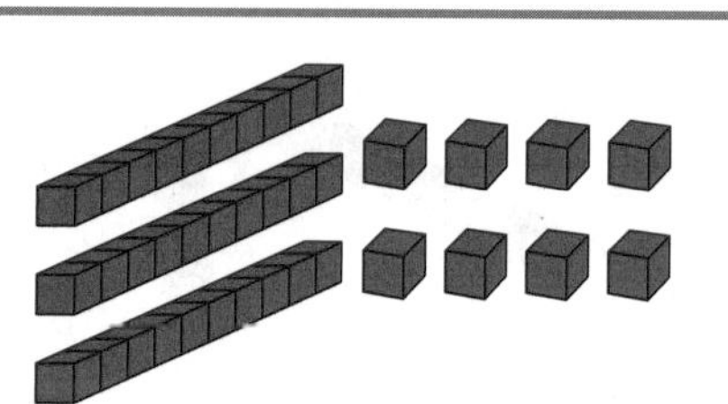

tens	ones

tens	ones

tens	ones

tens	ones

tens	ones

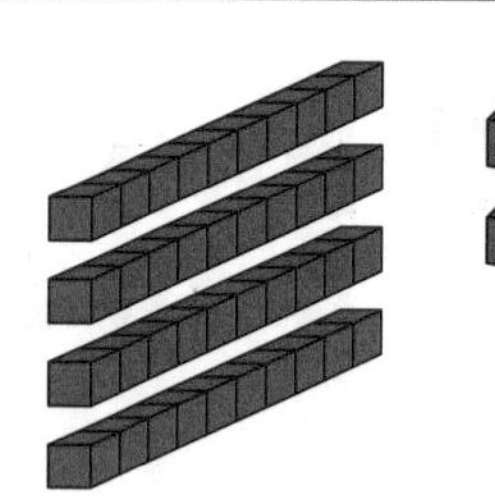

tens	ones

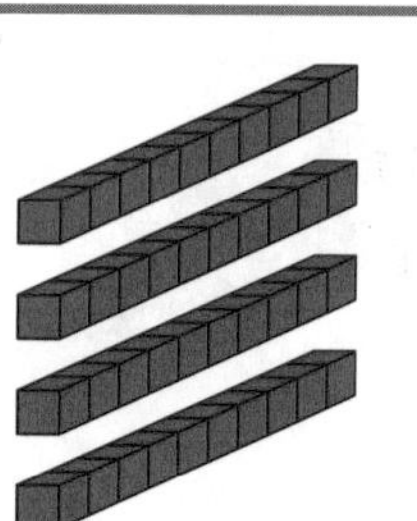

tens	ones

Make a calendar for next month. Keep track of the weather by drawing the symbols.

Sunday	Monday	Tuesday	Wednesday	Thursday	Friday	Saturday

Start at 18 and connect the numbers in order.

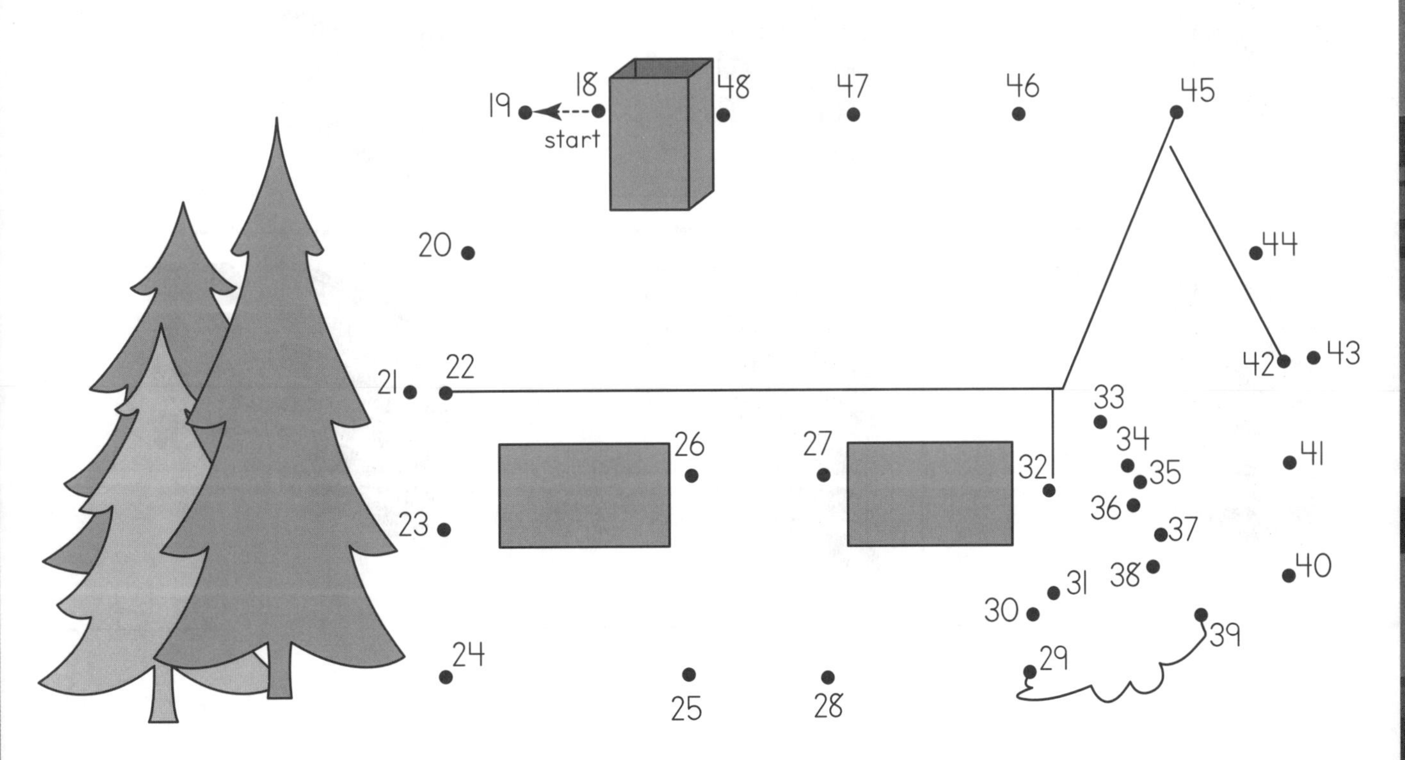

Write the number.

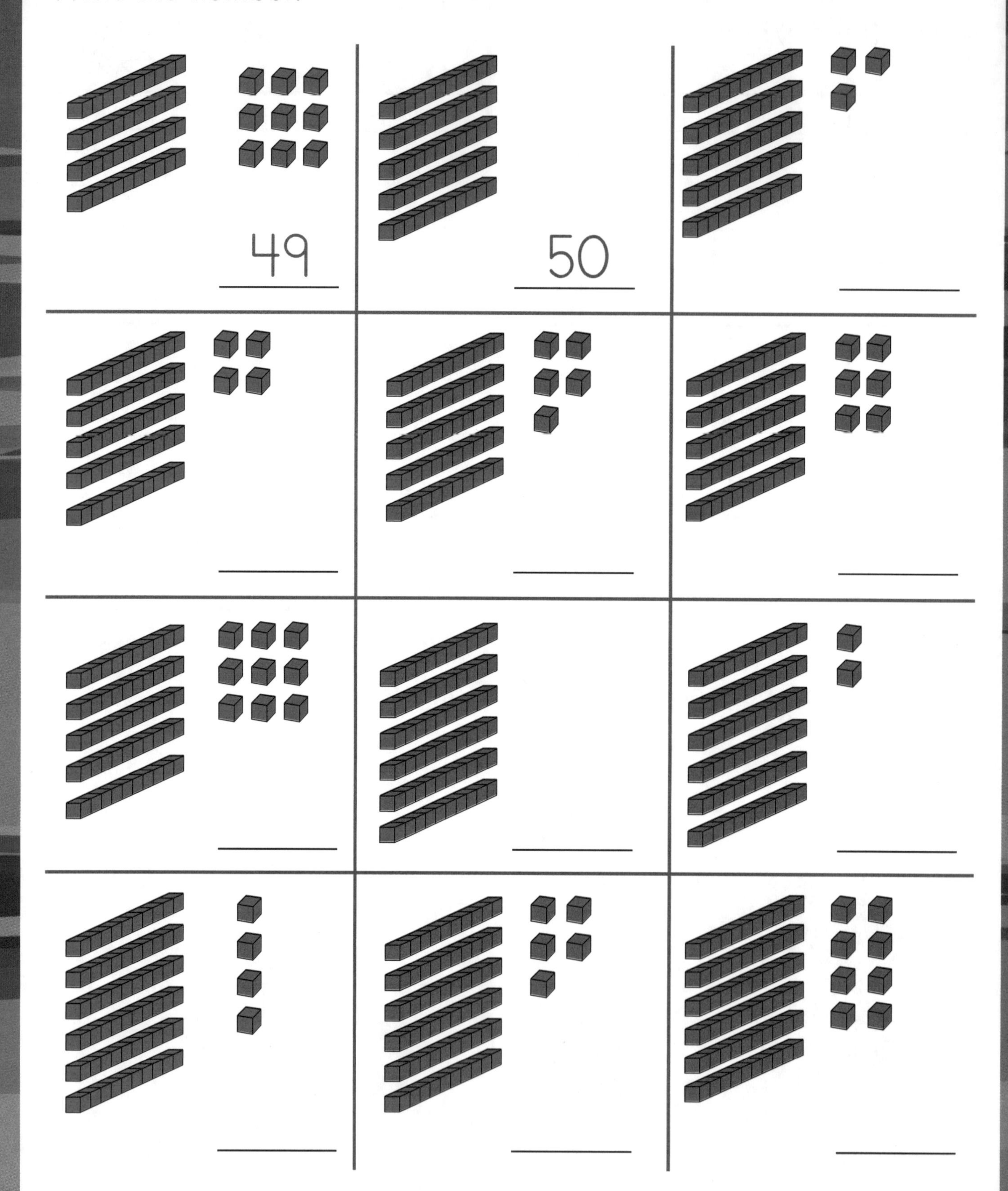

Write the number.

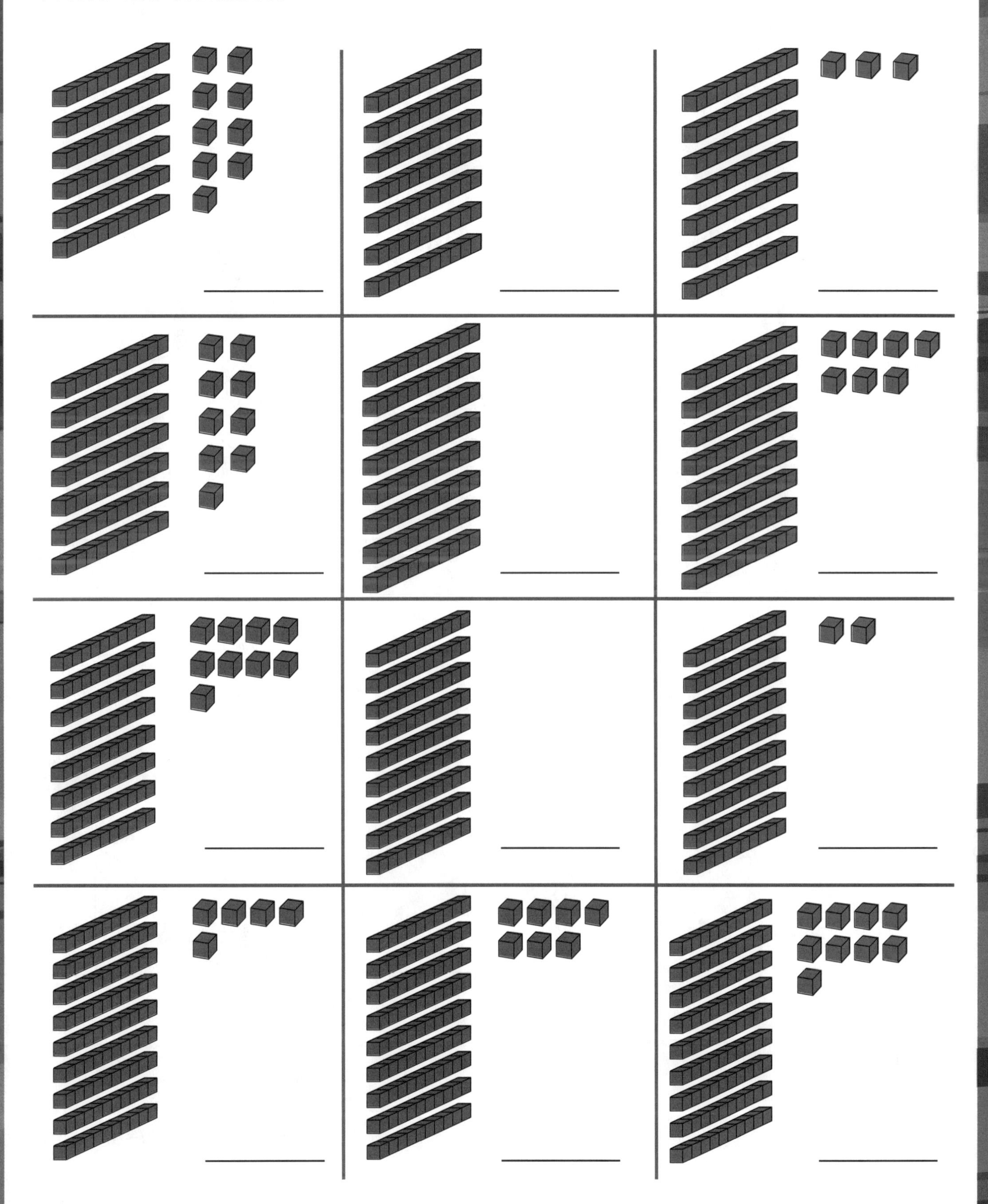

Count by tens to connect the dots.

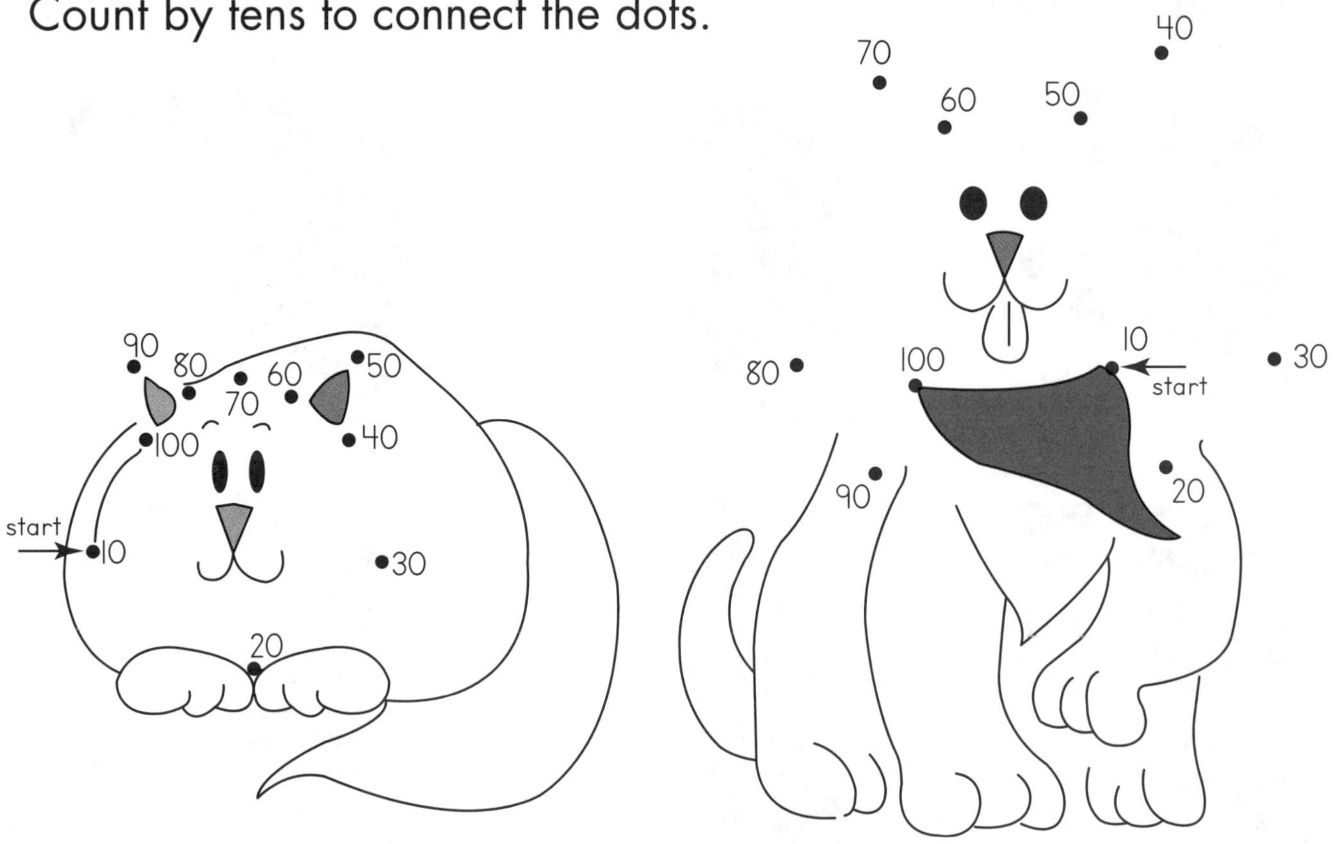

Count by fives to connect the dots.

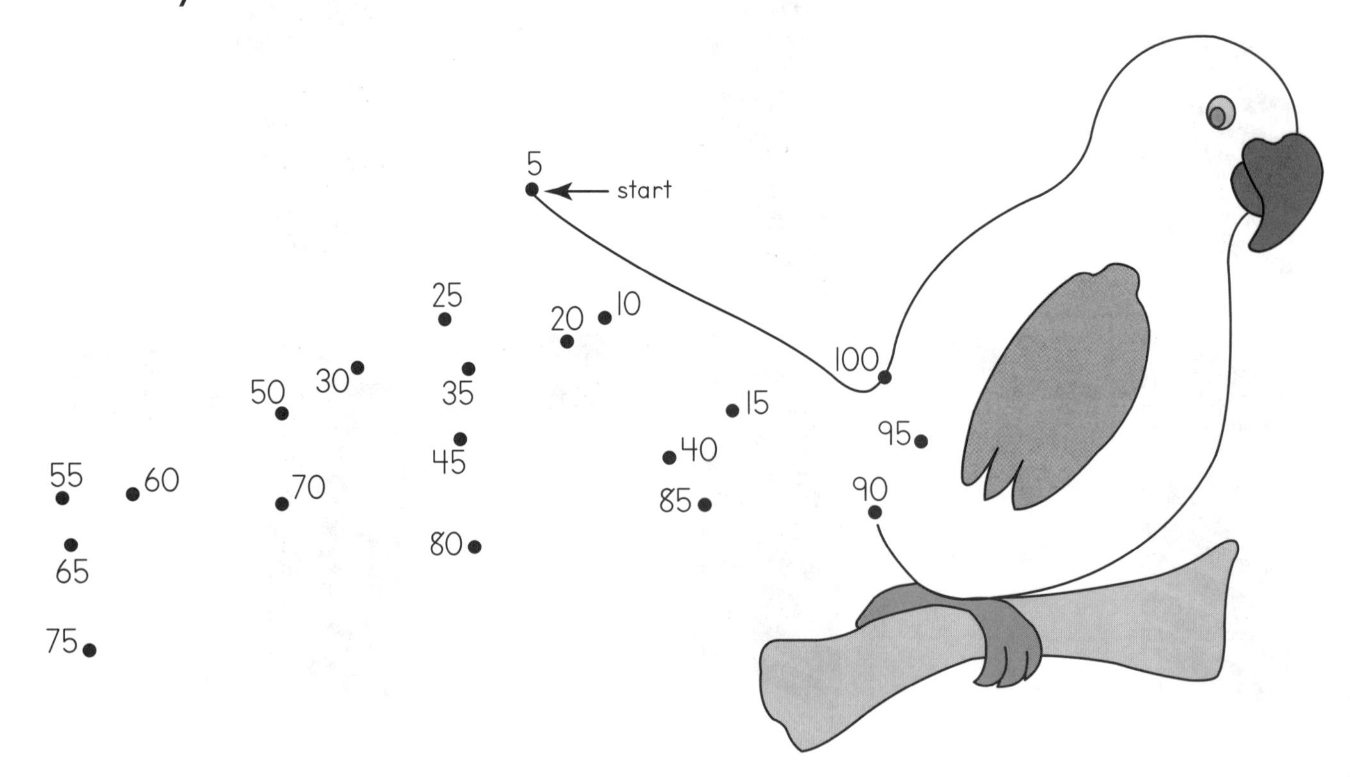

1¢

Write how much.

______ ¢

______ ¢

______ ¢

______ ¢

5¢

5¢

______ ¢

______ ¢

______ ¢

______ ¢

Write how much.

____ ¢

____ ¢

____ ¢

____ ¢

____ ¢

____ ¢

____ ¢

____ ¢

____ ¢

Write how much.

____ ¢

____ ¢

____ ¢

____ ¢

____ ¢

____ ¢

____ ¢

____ ¢

____ ¢

____ ¢

Write how much.

_______ ¢

_______ ¢

_______ ¢

_______ ¢

_______ ¢

_______ ¢

_______ ¢

_______ ¢

Garage sale! Circle the coins to buy each item.

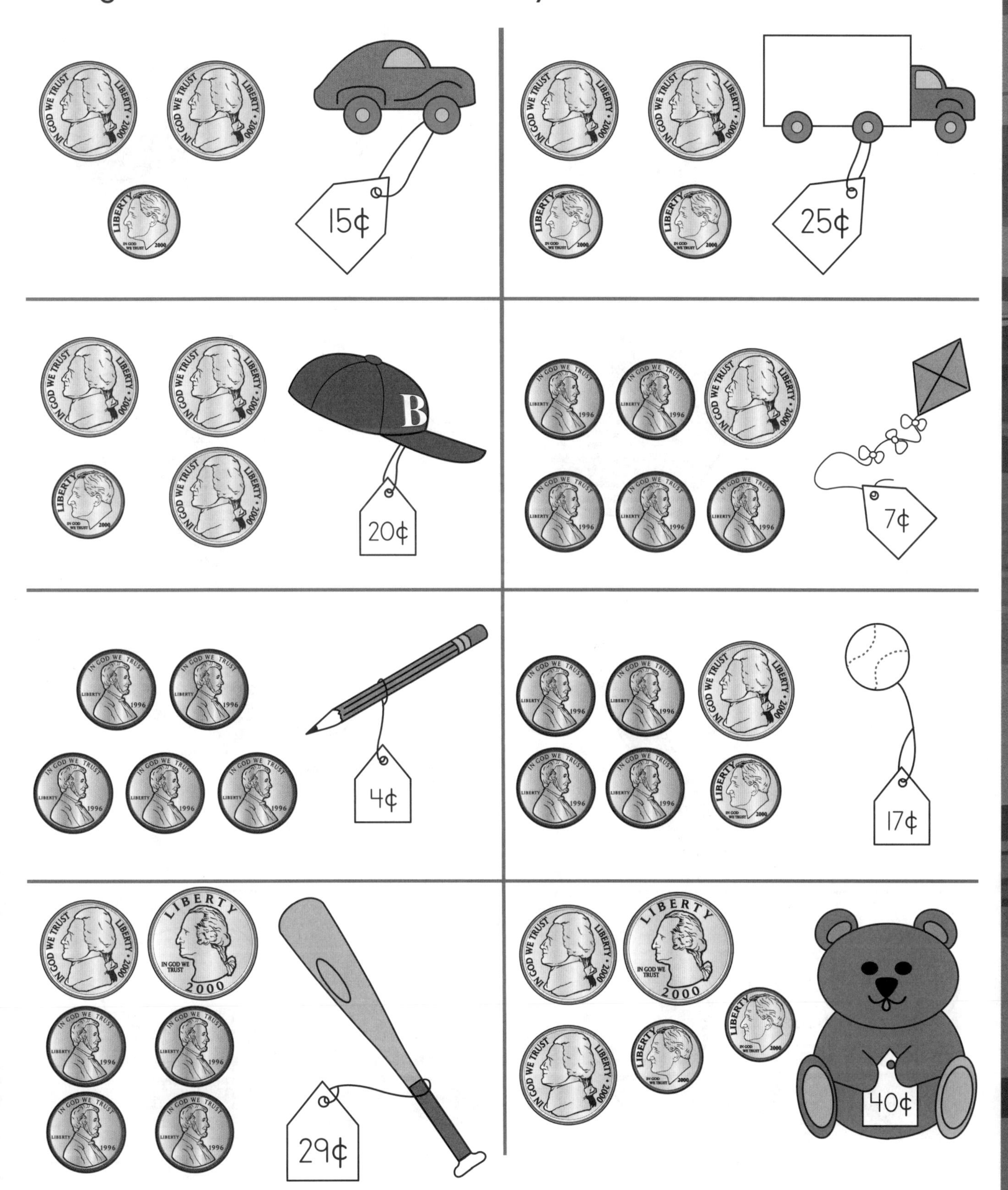

The coins shown pay for each item. Write how much it costs.

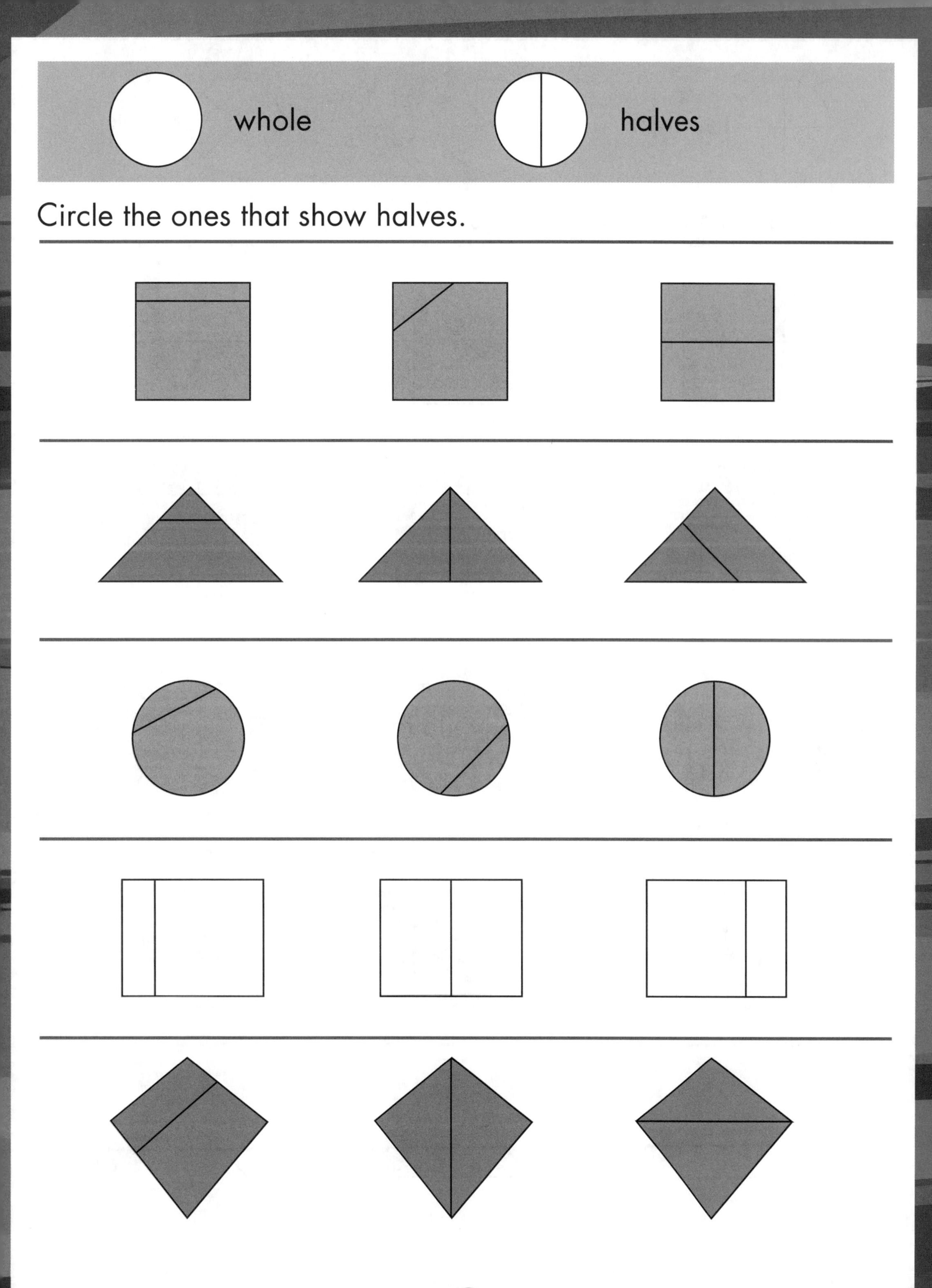
whole
halves
Circle the ones that show halves.

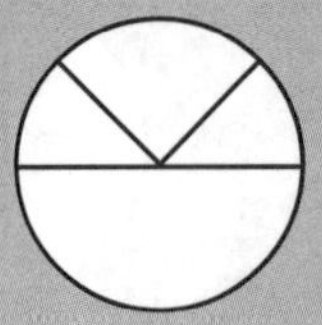

not fourths

Circle the ones that show fourths.

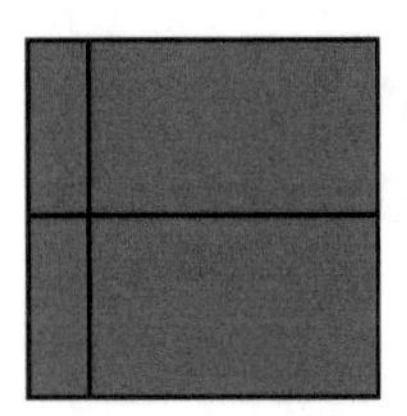
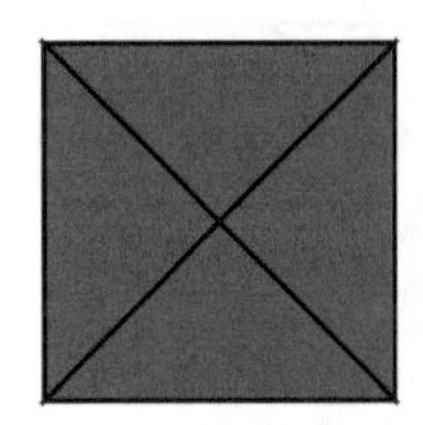
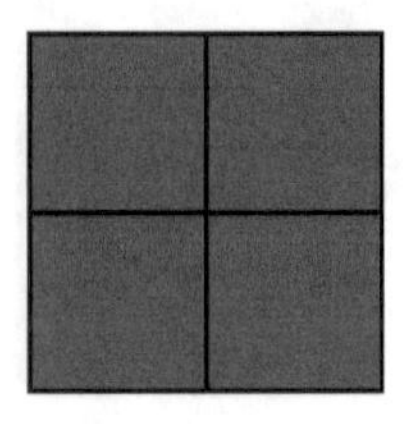

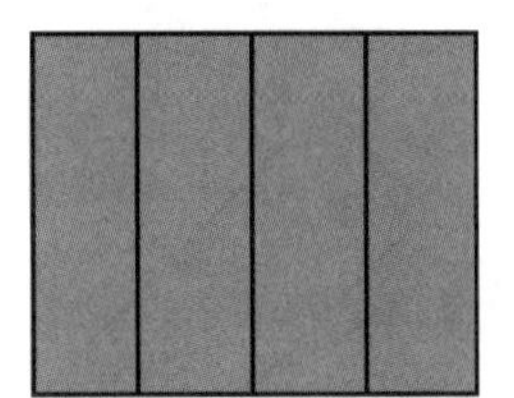
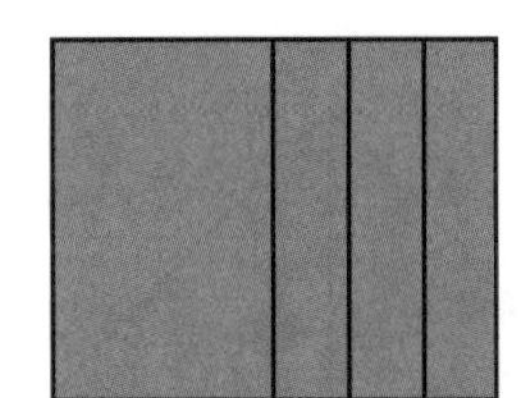
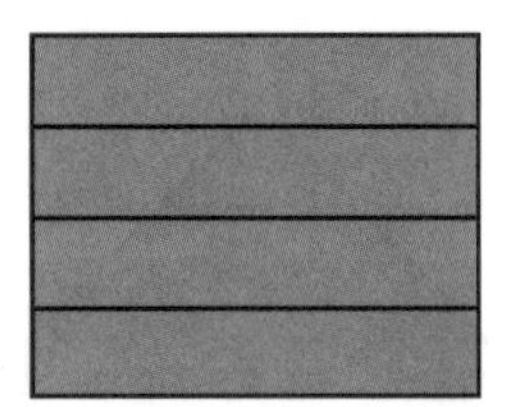

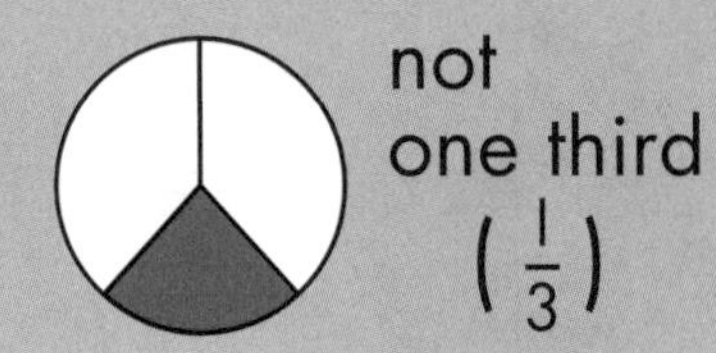

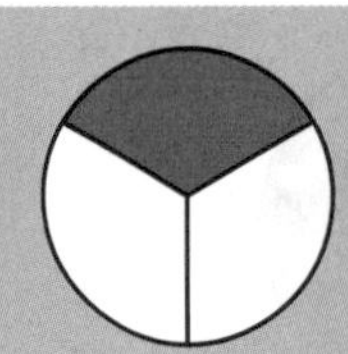

one third

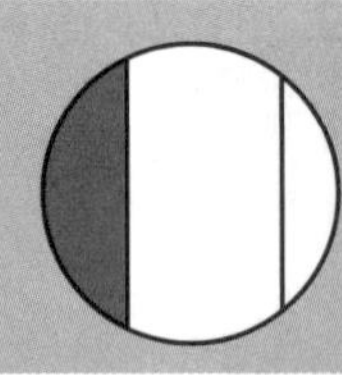

not
one third
($\frac{1}{3}$)

Circle the ones that show $\frac{1}{3}$.

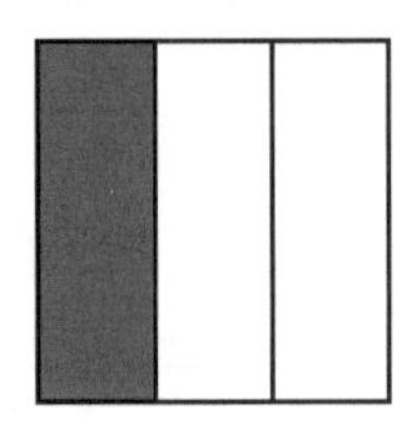
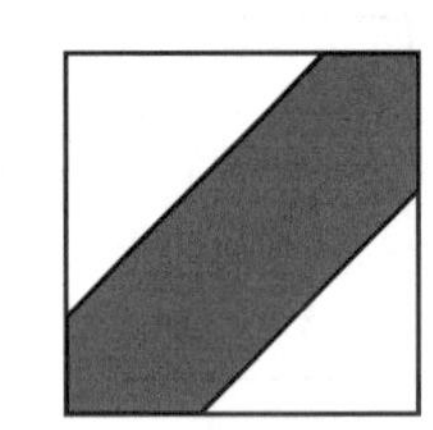

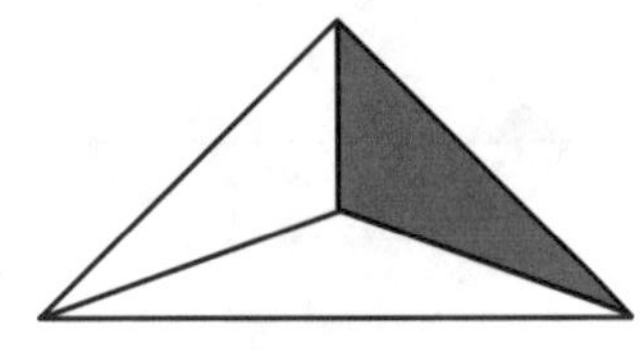
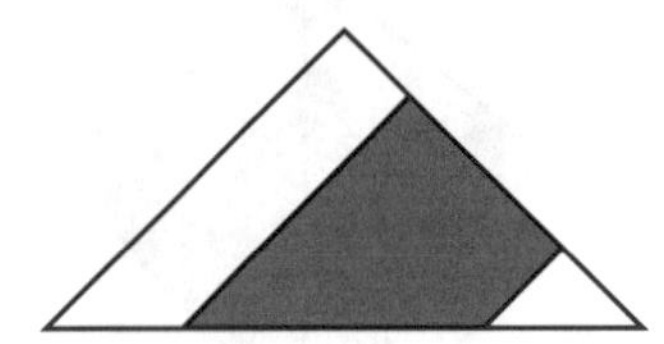
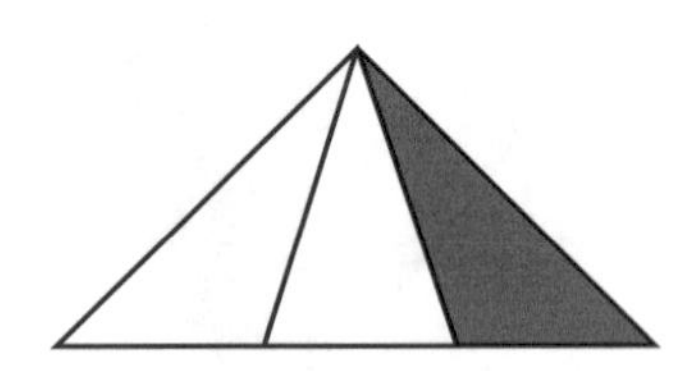

Color one half ($\frac{1}{2}$).

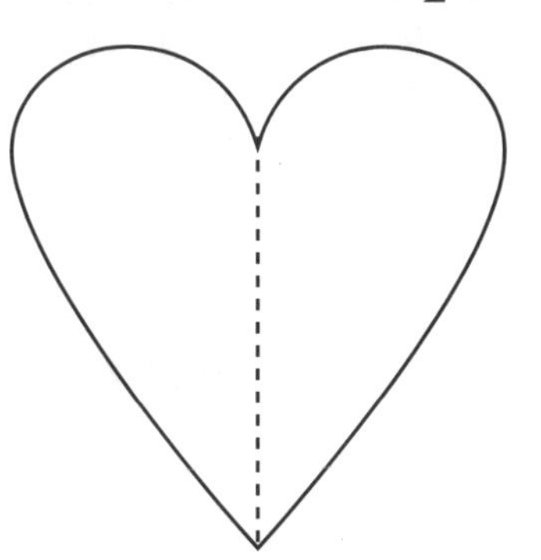
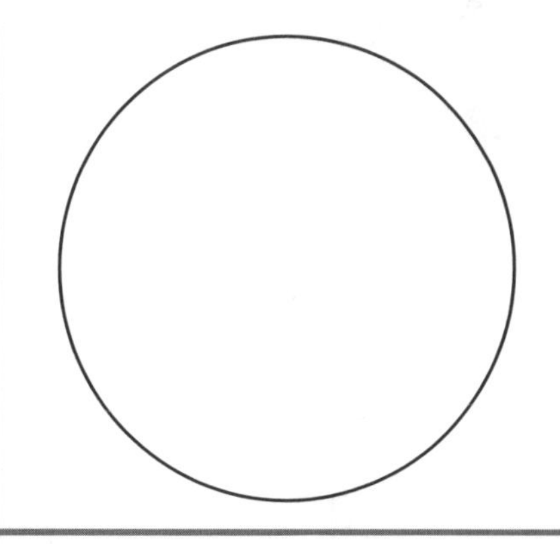

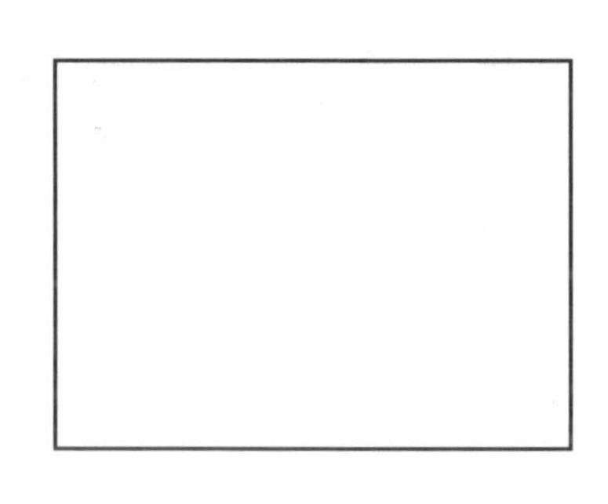
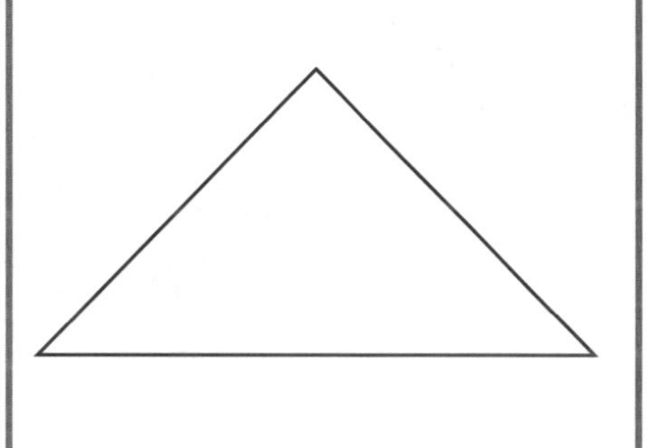
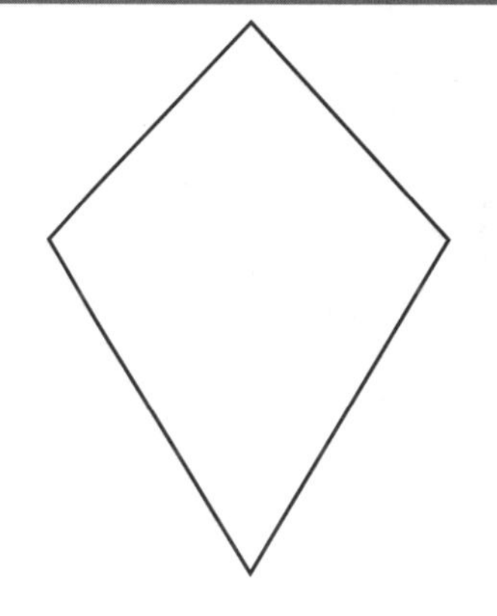

Color one fourth ($\frac{1}{4}$).

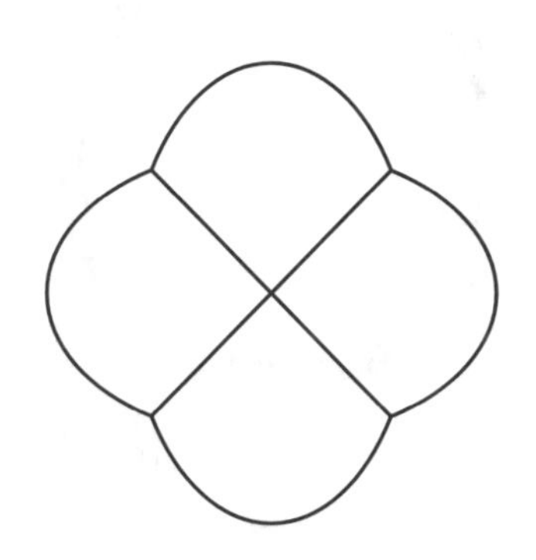
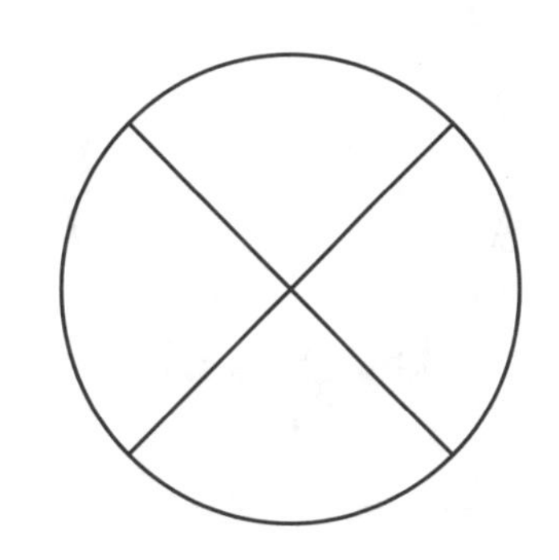
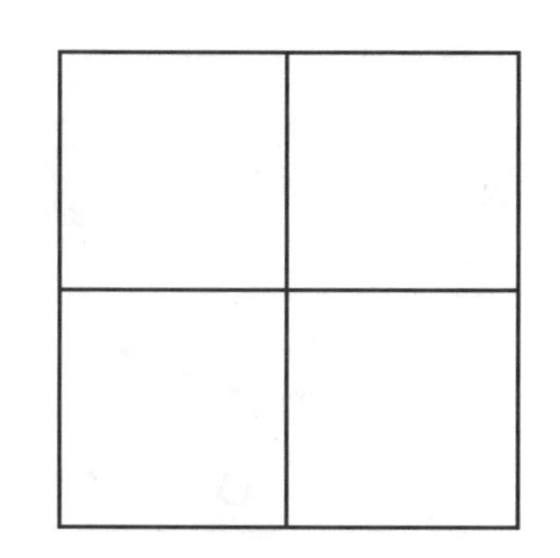
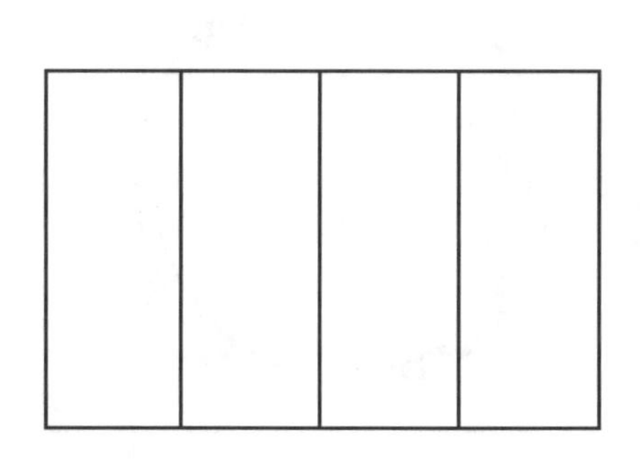
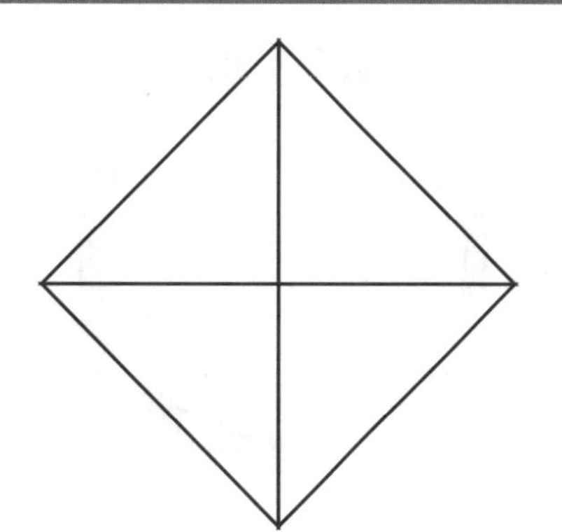
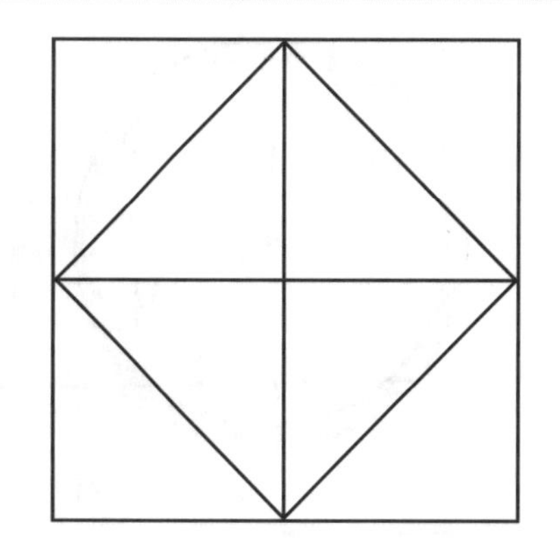

7 o'clock

What time is it?

_______ o'clock

_______ o'clock

_______ o'clock

_______ o'clock

_______ o'clock

_______ o'clock

_______ o'clock

_______ o'clock

Draw the hour hand to show the time.

4 o'clock

8 o'clock

10 o'clock

1 o'clock

12 o'clock

9 o'clock

Draw the hands to show the time.

7 o'clock

11 o'clock

2 o'clock

3 o'clock

5 o'clock

6 o'clock

What time is it?

9 o'clock

half past 8

half past ______

half past ______

half past ______

half past ______

half past ______

half past ______

half past ______

______ o'clock

half past ______

______ o'clock

Draw the minute hand to show the time.

half past 2

half past 5

half past 6

Draw the hour hand to show the time.

half past 8

half past 10

half past 12

Draw the hands to show the time.

half past 1

half past 3

half past 4

half past 7

half past 9

half past 11

What time is it?

_______ o'clock

half past _______

_______ o'clock

_______ o'clock

half past _______

half past _______

half past _______

_______ o'clock

half past _______

half past _______

half past _______

_______ o'clock

Match.

1. 

2. 

3. 

4. 

a. 12:30 b. 1:00 c. 6:00 d. 9:30

e. 9:00 f. 8:30 g. 3:30 h. 5:30

5. 

6.

7. 

8.

Color the watches.

11:30 **red** 11:00 **purple** 6:30 **green**

12:00 **yellow** 3:30 **blue** 1:30 **brown**

Trace the circle. Color all the circles.

Trace the rectangle. Color all the rectangles.

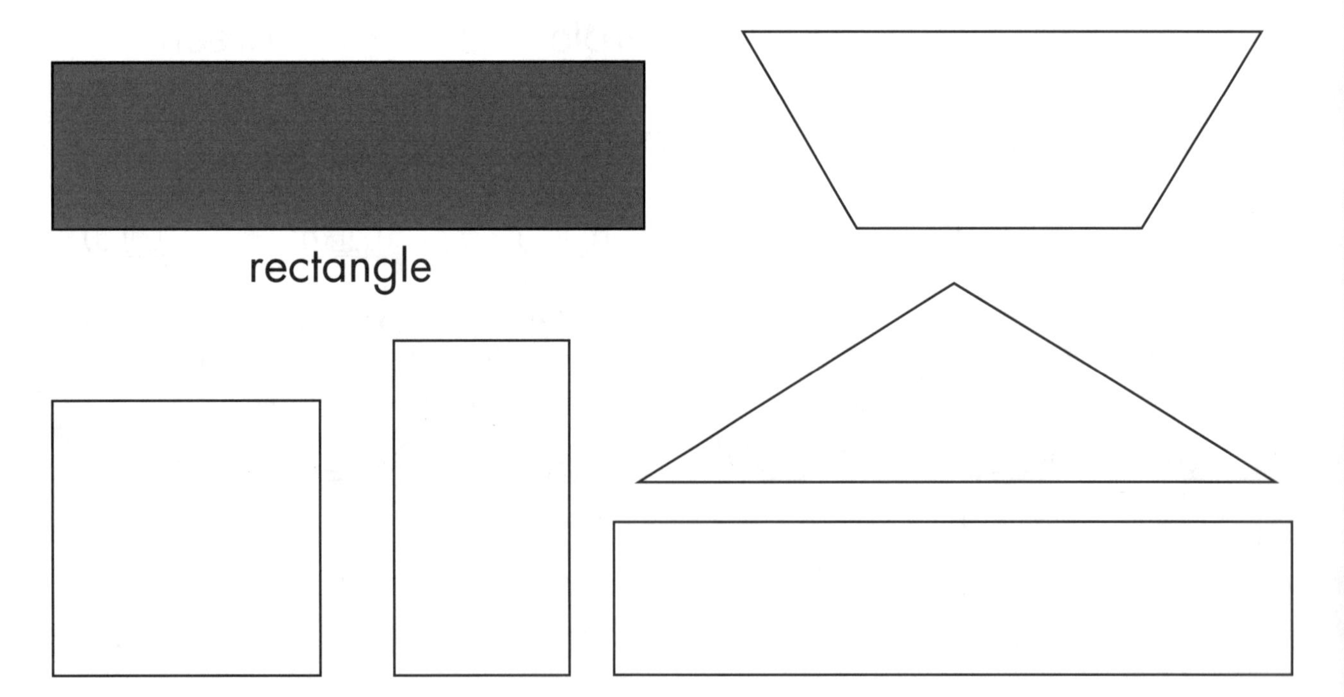

Trace the triangle. Color all the triangles.

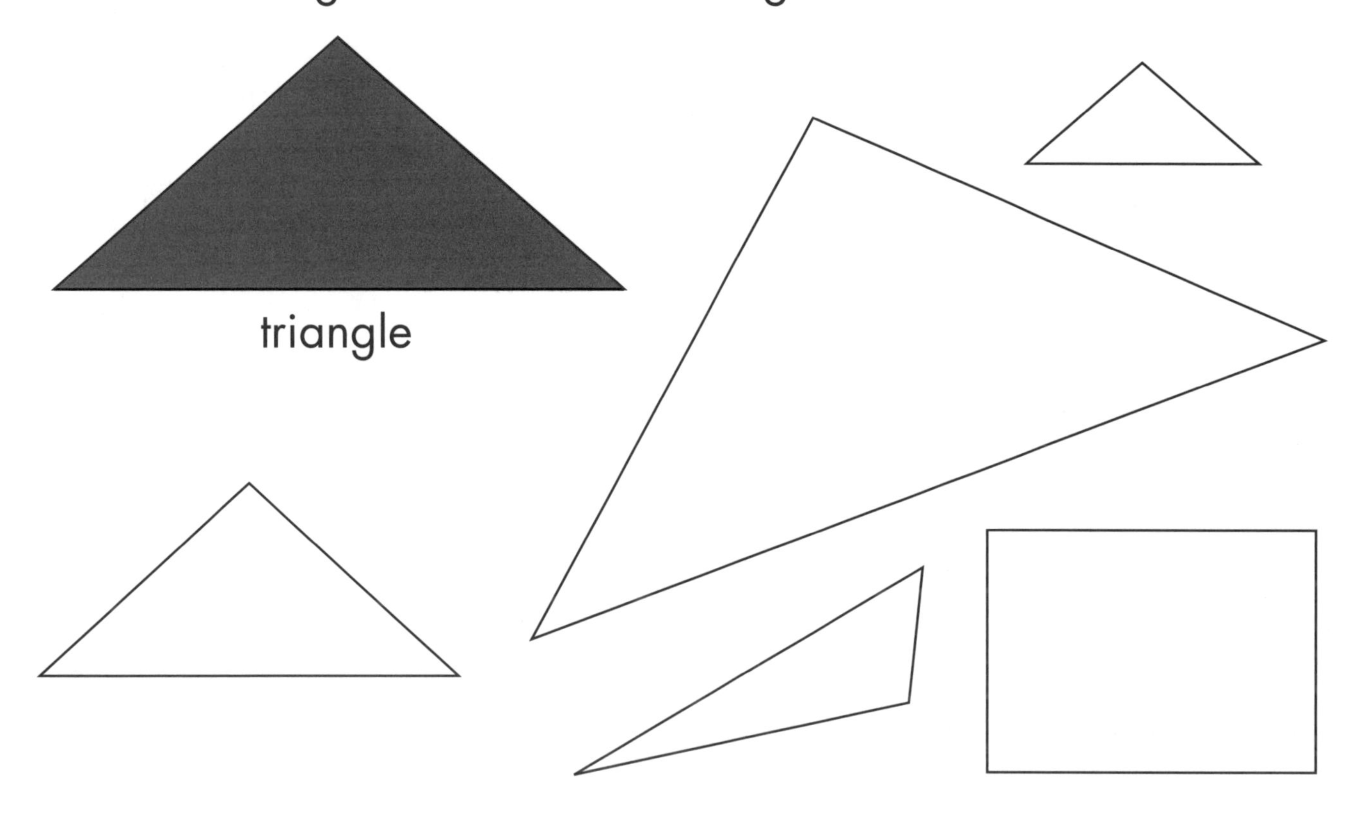

Trace the square. Color all the squares.

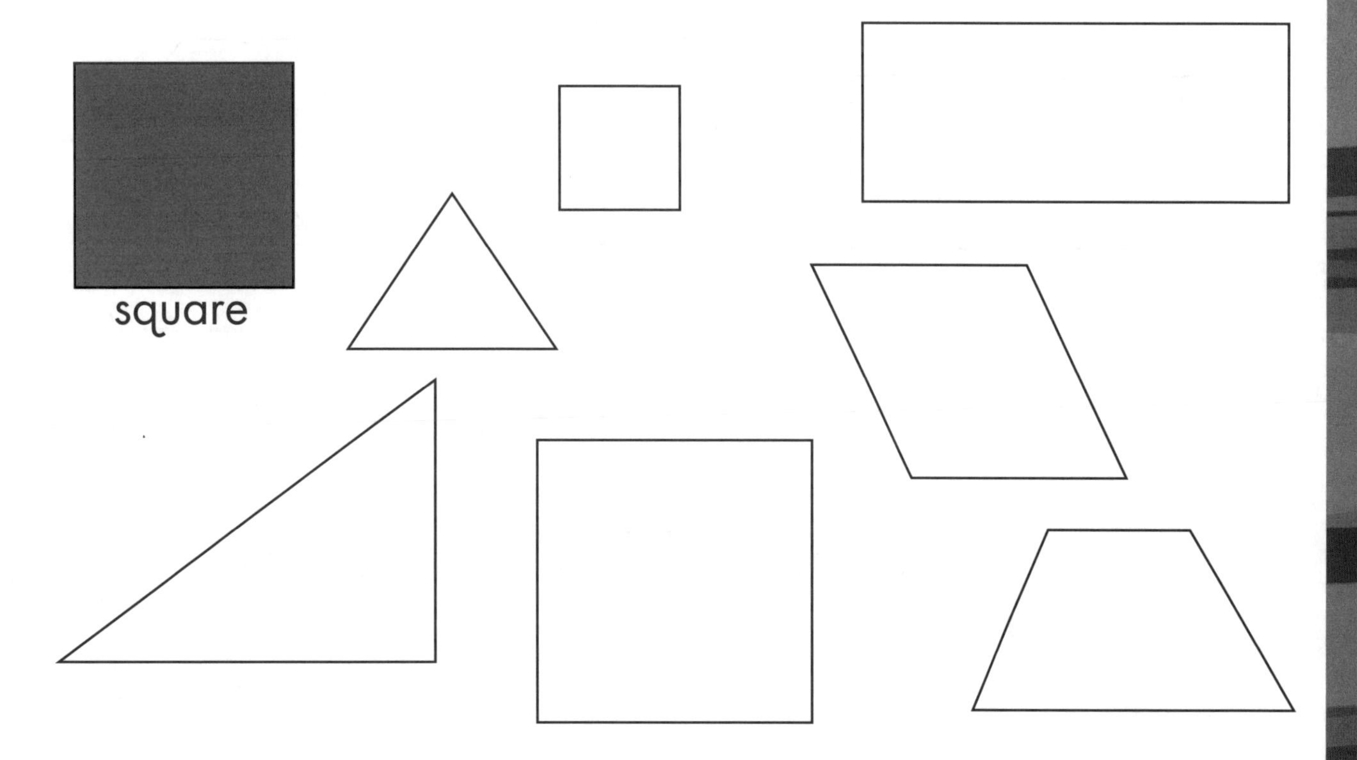

Color the shapes that are the same as the first.

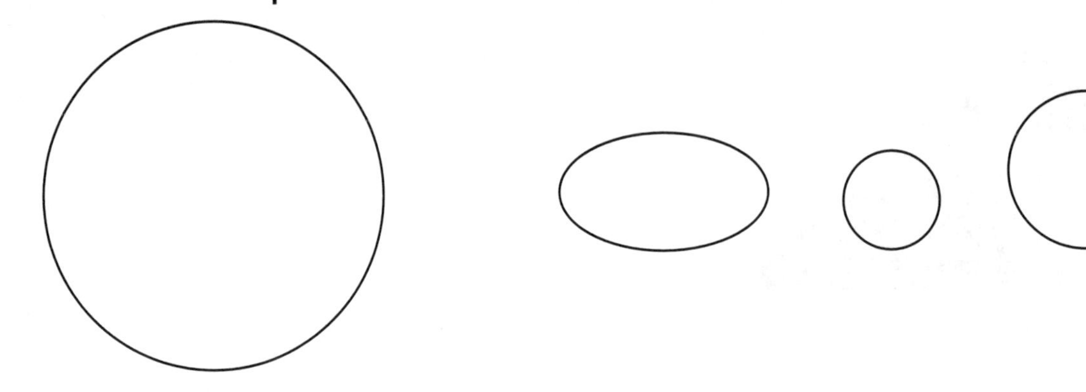

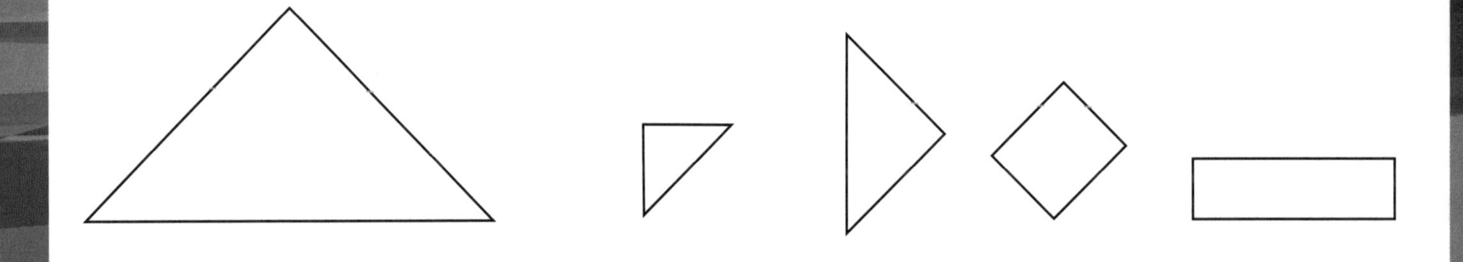

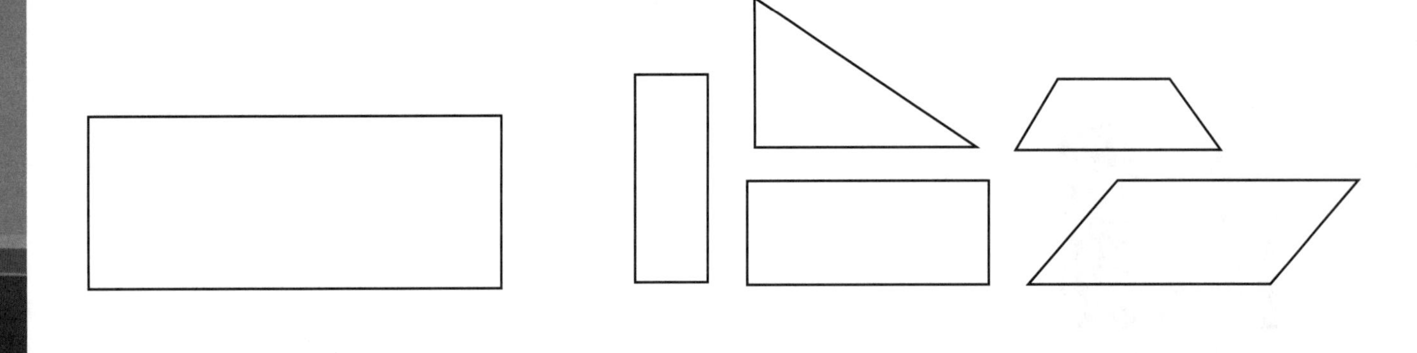

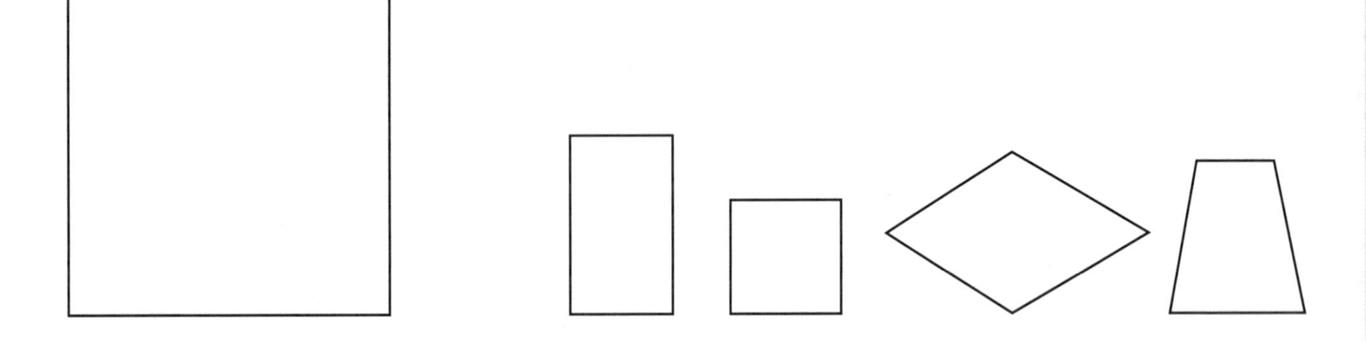

Color the shape that comes next.

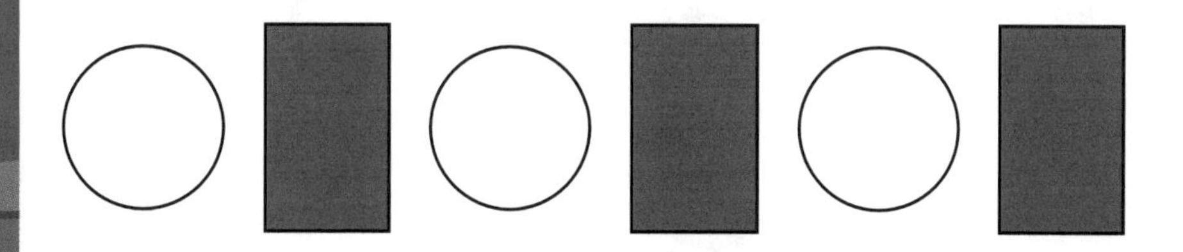
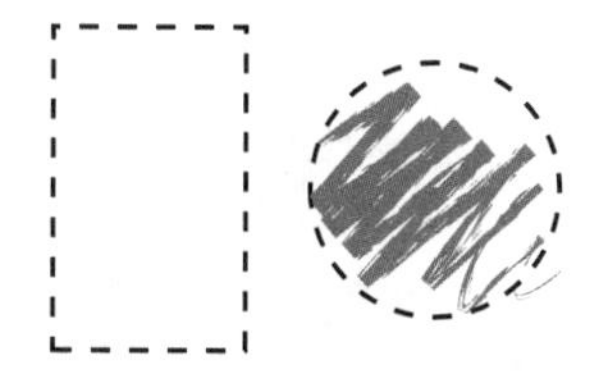

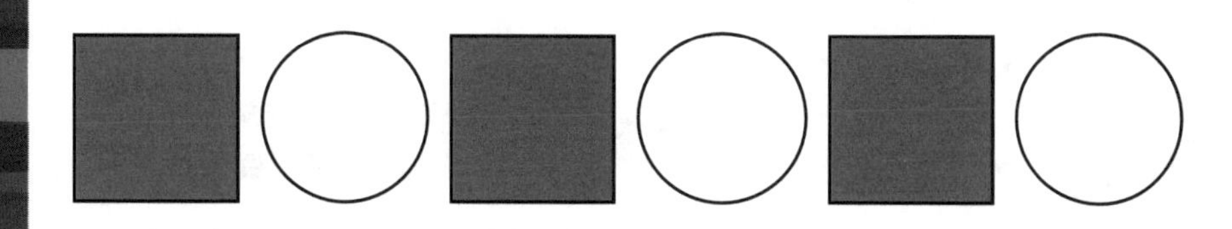
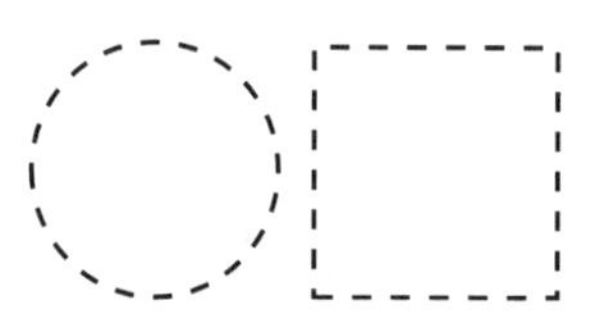

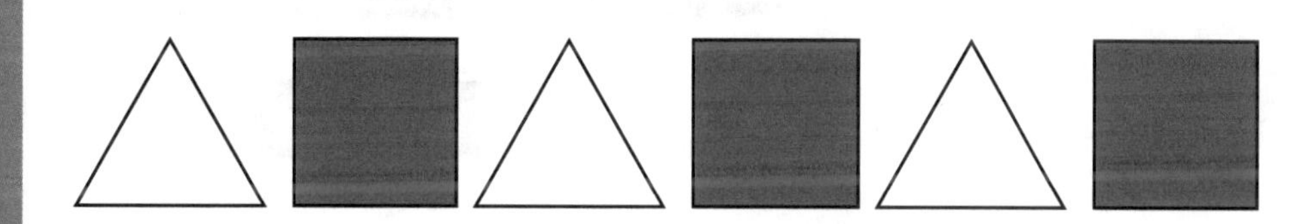

Draw the shapes that come next.

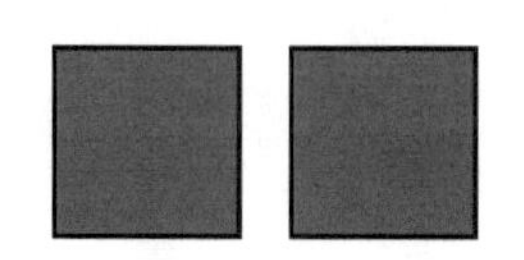
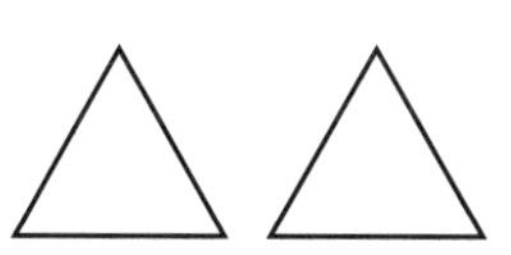
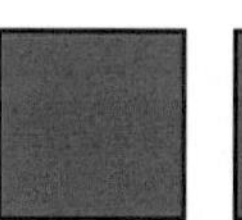

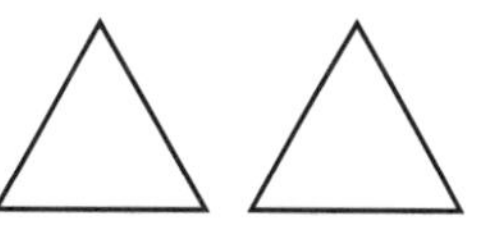

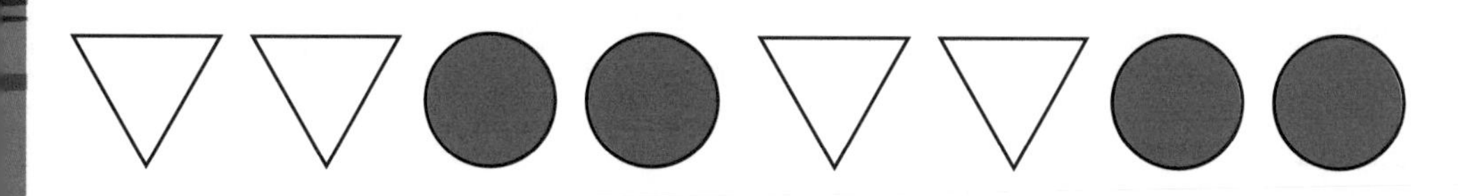

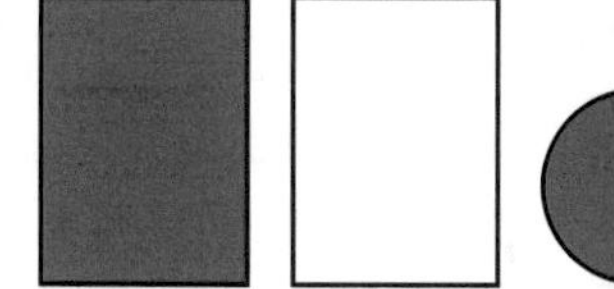
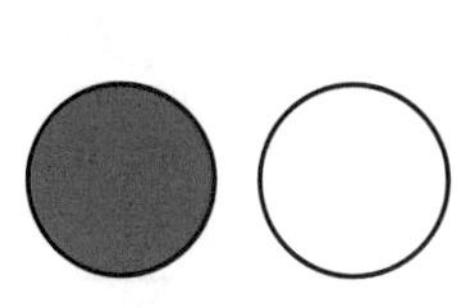

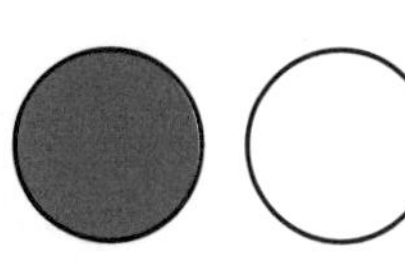

Circle the longest object.

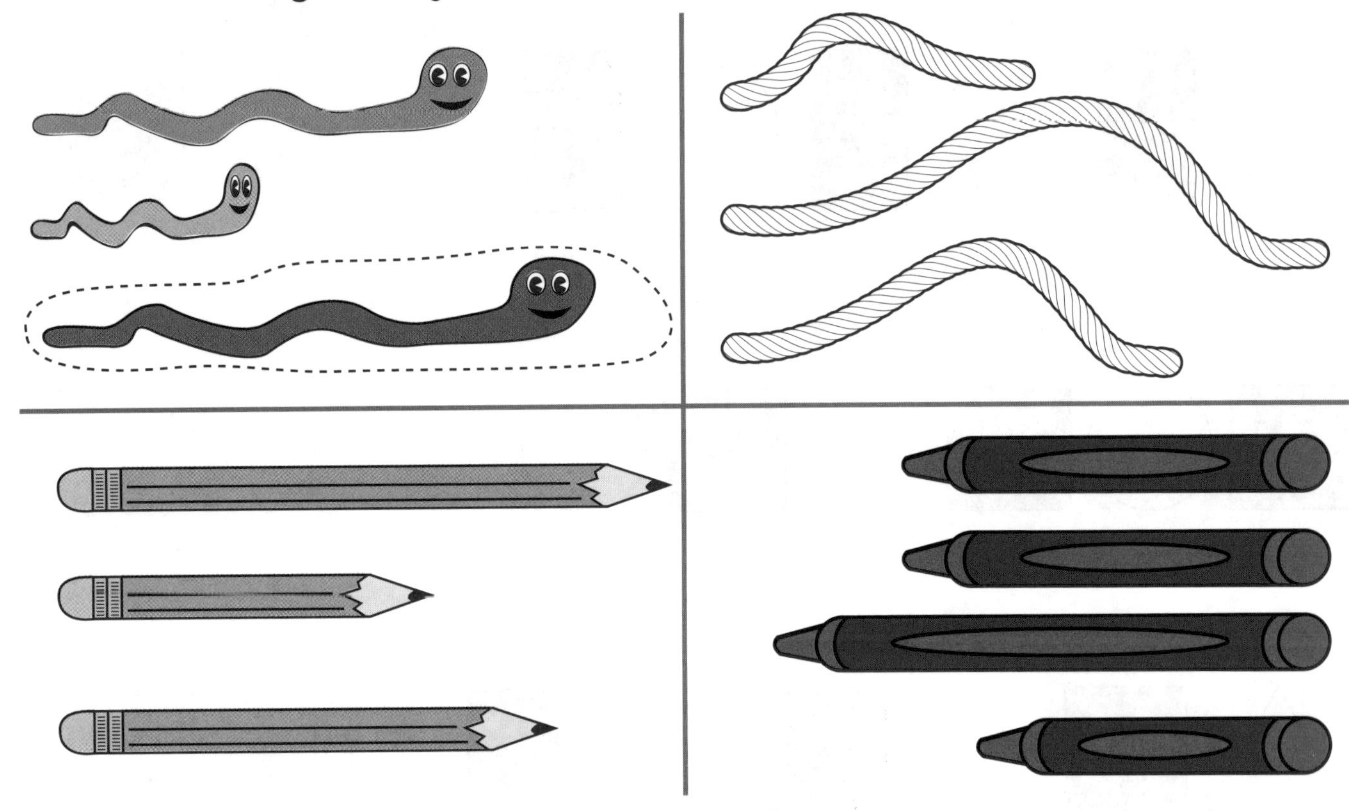

How many units long?

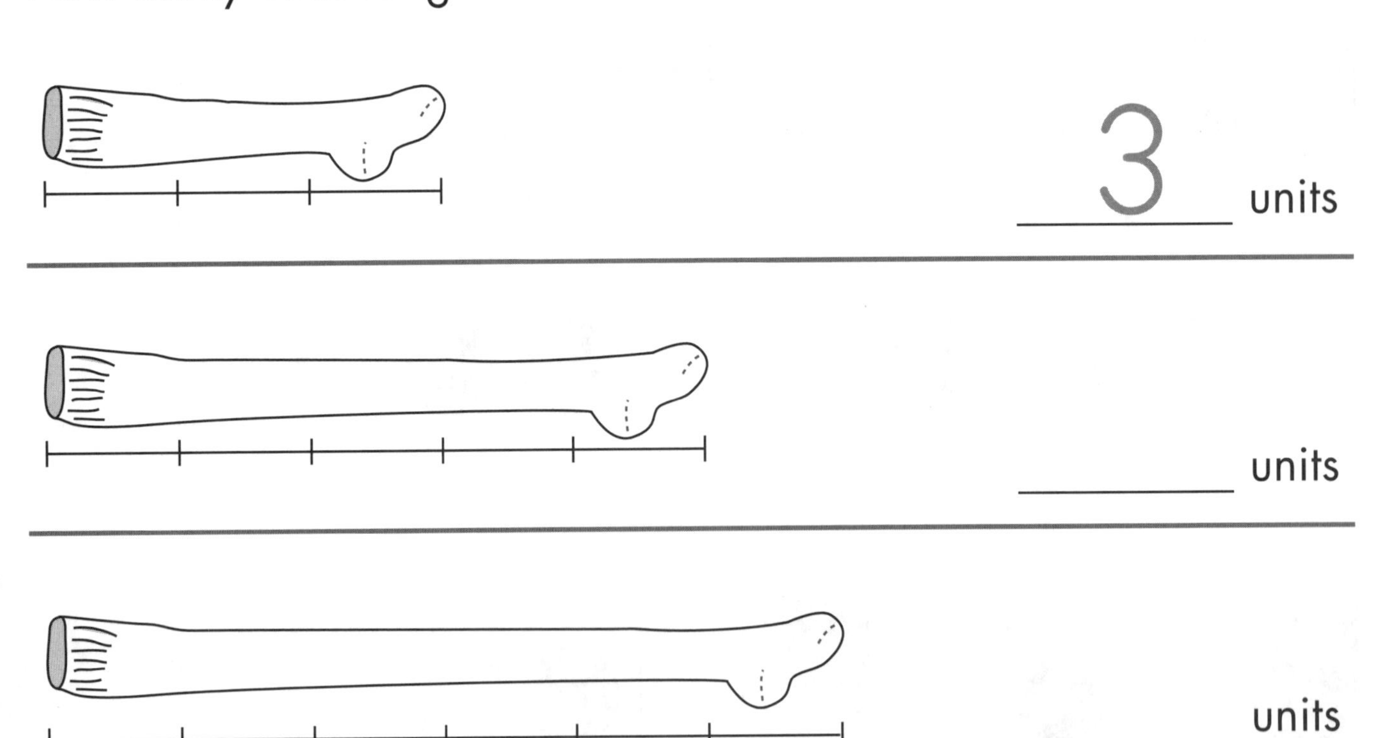

Write the weight.

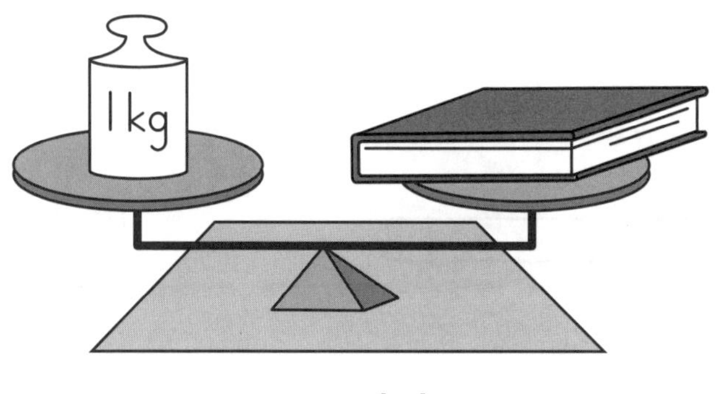

_____ kilogram

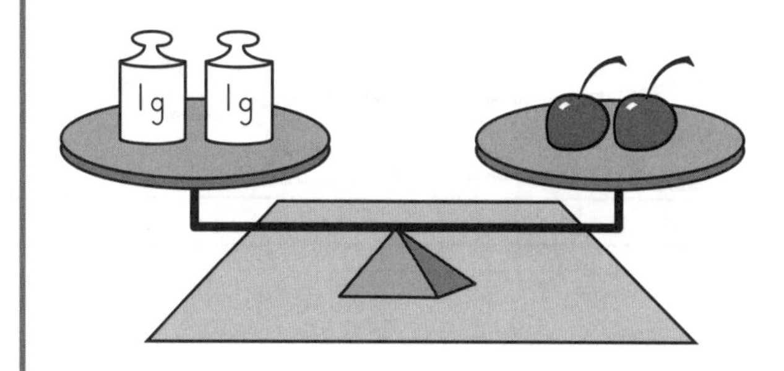

_____ grams

_____ ounces

_____ pounds

Circle which is lighter.

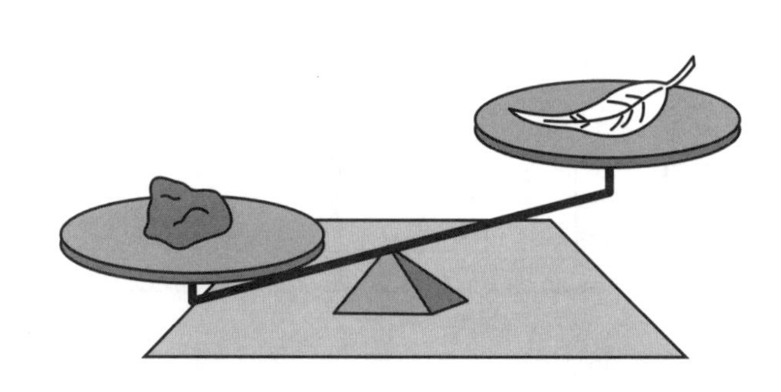

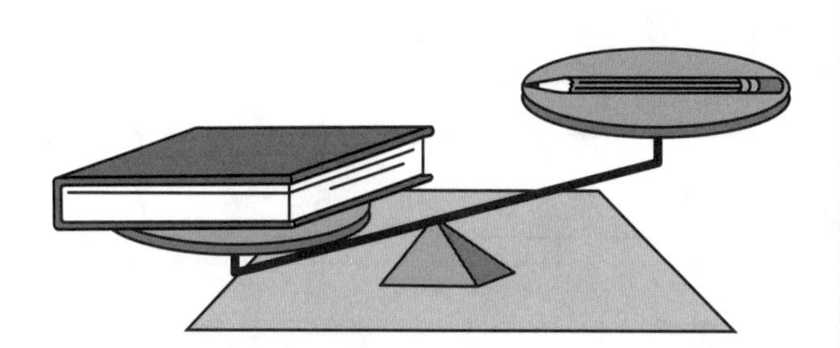

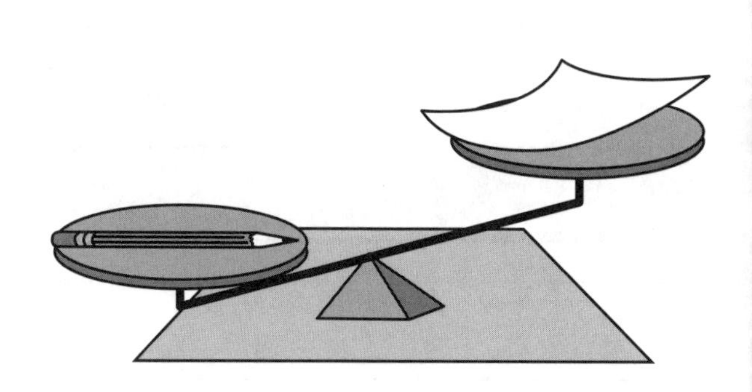

Write how long.

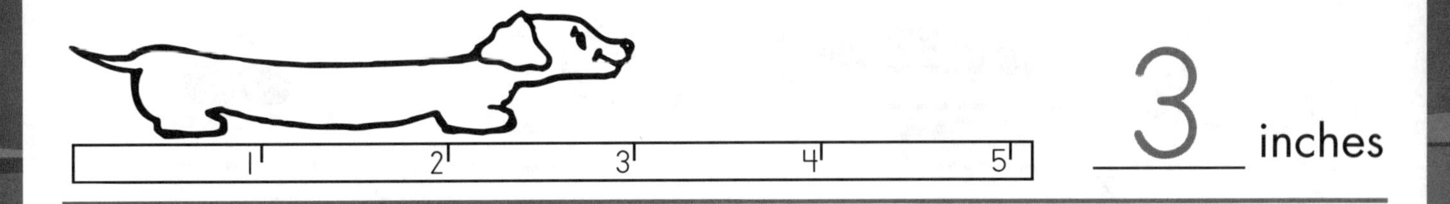

3 inches

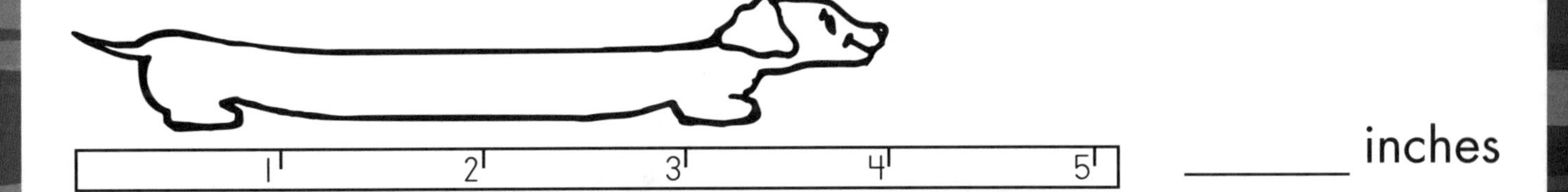

_____ inches

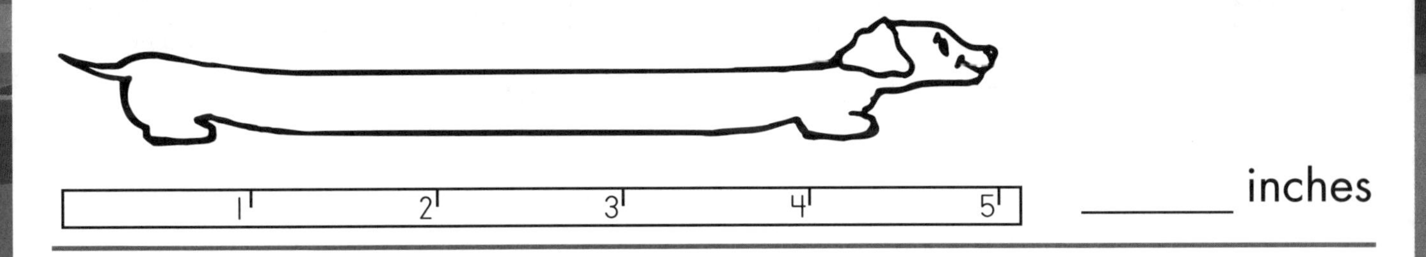

_____ inches

Write how long.

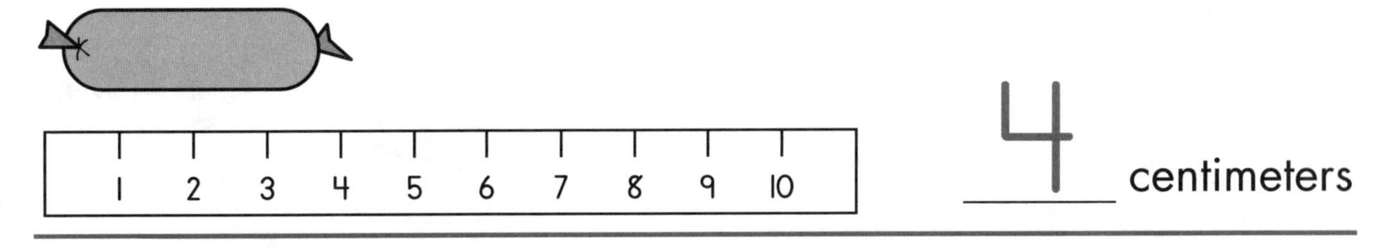

4 centimeters

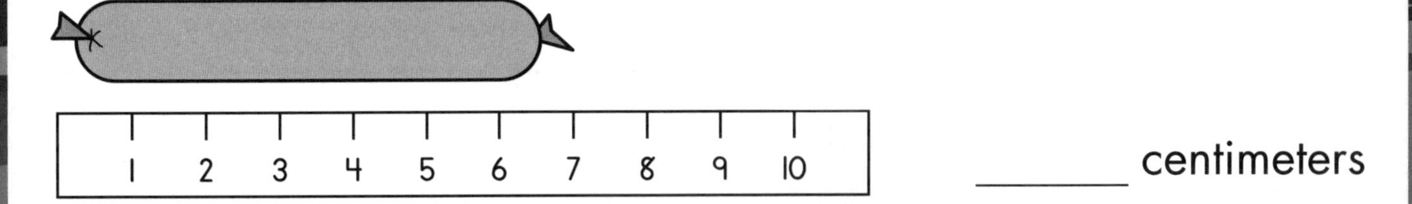

_____ centimeters

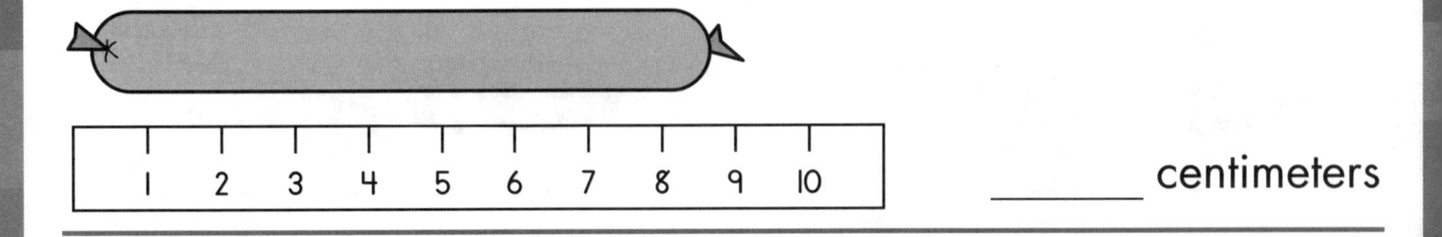

_____ centimeters

Circle the one that holds more.

How much does each hold?

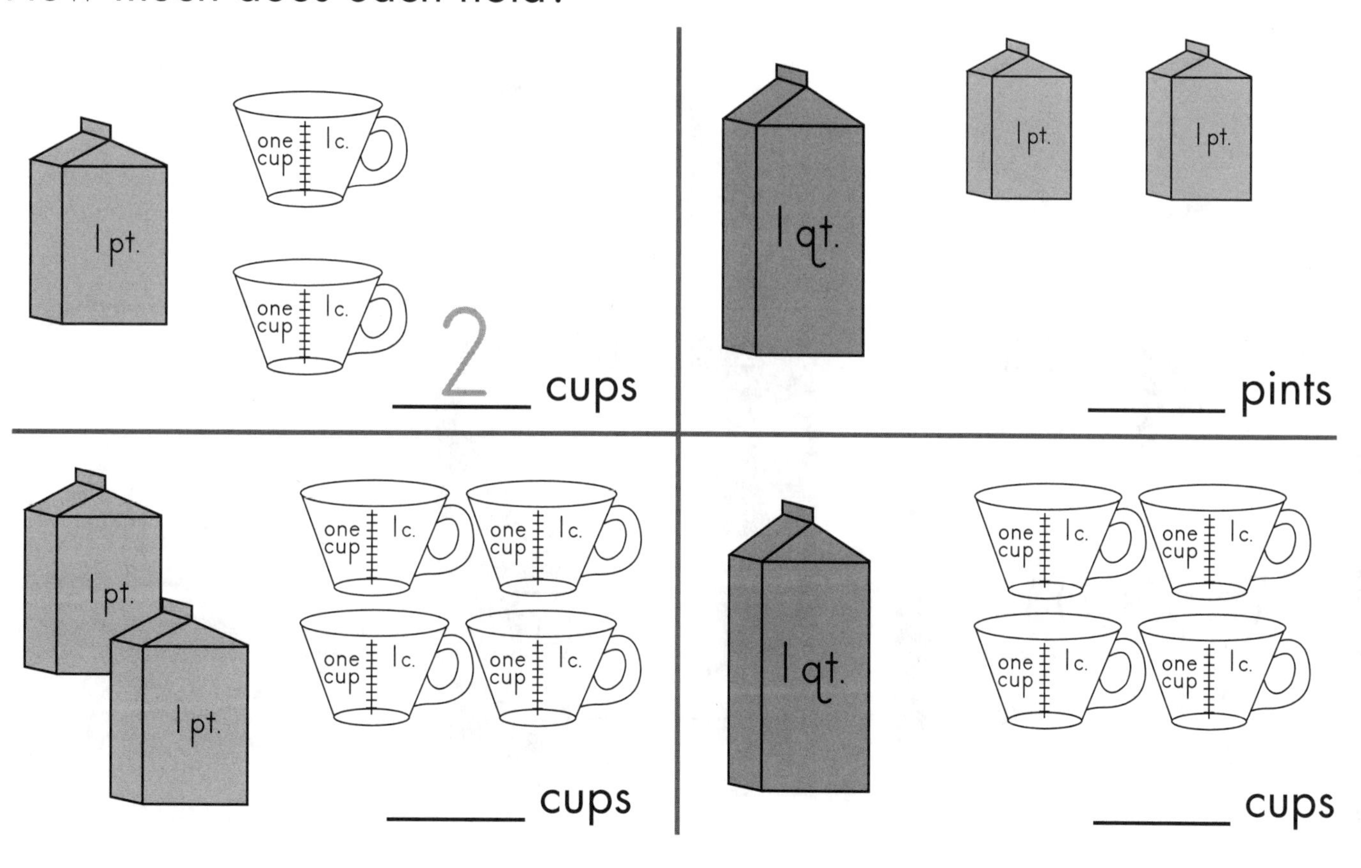

Which would you use to measure the things below?
Draw lines to match.

Add

4 + 3 = 7   2 + 4 =   3 + 3 =

1 + 4 =   2 + 3 =   2 + 2 =

4 + 4 =   3 + 1 =   1 + 0 =

1 + 1 =   1 + 2 =   4 + 5 =

5 + 1 = 6   6 + 2 =   5 + 2 =

4 + 0 =   5 + 0 =   7 + 2 =

3 + 4 =   8 + 1 =   7 + 1 =

6 + 1 =   6 + 3 =   2 + 0 =

Add.

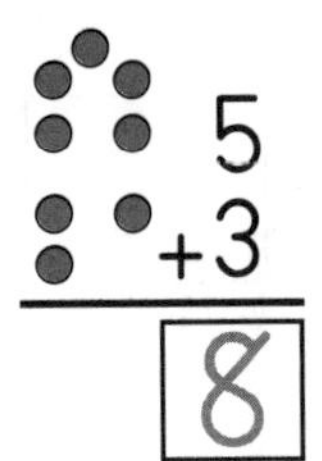

$5 + 3 = 8$	$9 + 1$	$6 + 0$	$5 + 4$	$5 + 5$
$5 + 6$	$7 + 6$	$8 + 3$	$6 + 4$	$9 + 2$
$7 + 4$	$8 + 2$	$7 + 3$	$6 + 6$	$6 + 5$
$6 + 7 = 13$	$8 + 5$	$9 + 6$	$8 + 6$	$9 + 3$
$7 + 7$	$8 + 4$	$7 + 5$	$8 + 8$	$7 + 8$
$9 + 7$	$9 + 4$	$9 + 5$	$9 + 8$	$9 + 9$

Subtract.

$4 - 2 = \boxed{2}$ | $5 - 2 = \boxed{}$ | $6 - 4 = \boxed{}$

$8 - 1 = \boxed{}$ | $7 - 4 = \boxed{}$ | $5 - 3 = \boxed{}$

$4 - 3 = \boxed{}$ | $3 - 2 = \boxed{}$ | $4 - 1 = \boxed{}$

$3 - 1 = \boxed{}$ | $7 - 2 = \boxed{}$ | $5 - 4 = \boxed{}$

$6 - 1 = \boxed{5}$ | $7 - 3 = \boxed{}$ | $7 - 6 = \boxed{}$

$7 - 5 = \boxed{}$ | $6 - 2 = \boxed{}$ | $7 - 1 = \boxed{}$

$9 - 0 = \boxed{}$ | $9 - 1 = \boxed{}$ | $6 - 3 = \boxed{}$

$8 - 3 = \boxed{}$ | $8 - 2 = \boxed{}$ | $9 - 2 = \boxed{}$

Subtract.

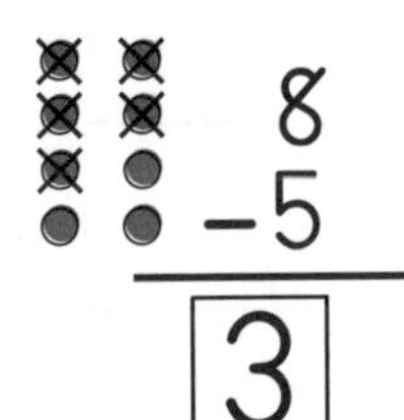
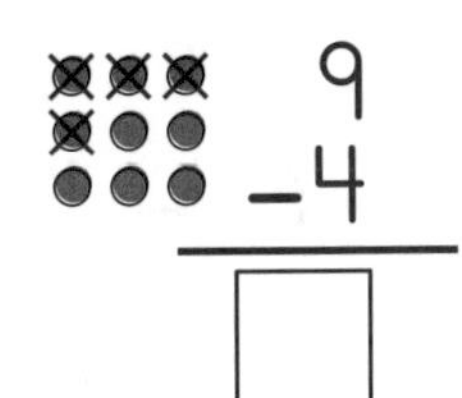

$8 - 5 = \boxed{3}$	$9 - 4 = \boxed{}$	$10 - 1 = \boxed{}$	$9 - 5 = \boxed{}$	$9 - 3 = \boxed{}$
$10 - 3 = \boxed{}$	$10 - 5 = \boxed{}$	$8 - 4 = \boxed{}$	$10 - 2 = \boxed{}$	$10 - 4 = \boxed{}$
$11 - 6 = \boxed{}$	$12 - 5 = \boxed{}$	$11 - 8 = \boxed{}$	$11 - 4 = \boxed{}$	$11 - 2 = \boxed{}$

$12 - 3 = \boxed{9}$	$14 - 5 = \boxed{}$	$12 - 8 = \boxed{}$	$14 - 6 = \boxed{}$	$13 - 9 = \boxed{}$
$13 - 5 = \boxed{}$	$13 - 6 = \boxed{}$	$12 - 6 = \boxed{}$	$14 - 7 = \boxed{}$	$15 - 9 = \boxed{}$
$15 - 7 = \boxed{}$	$16 - 7 = \boxed{}$	$16 - 8 = \boxed{}$	$17 - 8 = \boxed{}$	$18 - 9 = \boxed{}$

Review.

Circle how many.

2 3 4

4 5 6

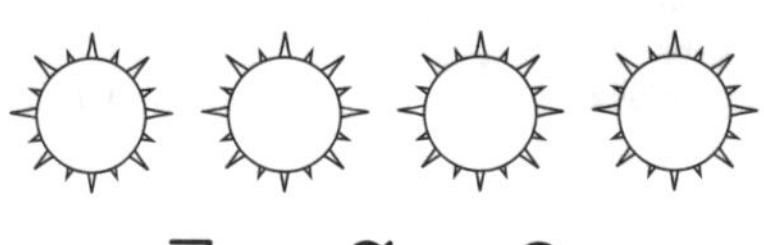

7 8 9

Write how many.

_____
_____
_____

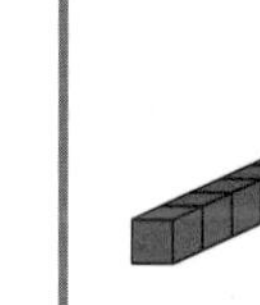 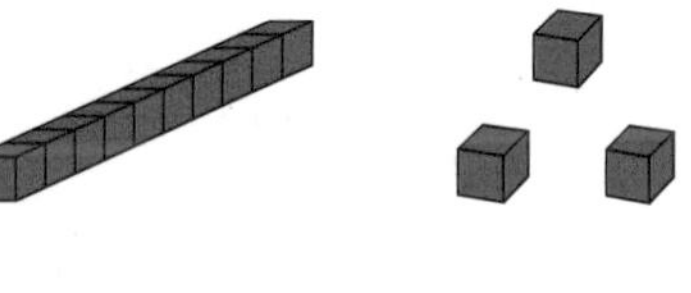

_____ten _____ones

_____tens _____ones

Write how much.

_____¢

Match.

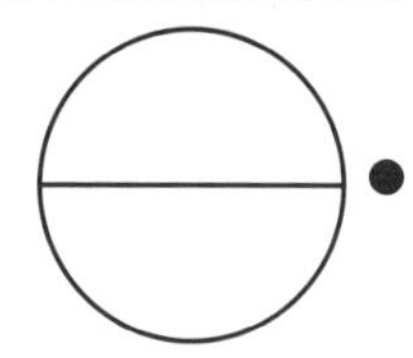 • • fourths

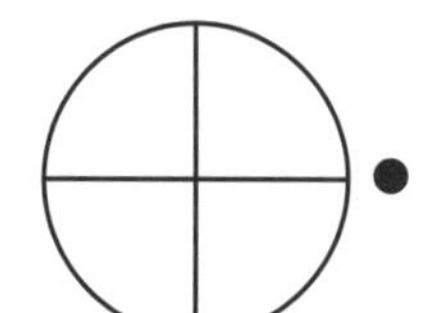 • • halves

1:30 • • 

11:00 • • 

Add.

4 + 1 = ☐

$$\begin{array}{r} 8 \\ +6 \\ \hline \end{array}$$

Subtract.

7 − 3 = ☐

$$\begin{array}{r} 16 \\ -8 \\ \hline \end{array}$$

Answer Key

3
0 1
1 0
Check students' writing.
1 0
0 1

4
The groups of oranges, pears, and watermelons should be colored; lemons and cherries should be circled.
Check students' drawings.

5
3 2 1
2 1 3
Check students' writing.
2 3
3 2

6
The groups of softballs, volleyballs, and baseballs should be colored.
Check students' drawings.

7
3 4 4
3 3 3
Check students' writing.
4 3
3 4

8
The groups of snails, dolphins, and sharks should be circled.
Check students' drawings.

9
4 5 5
5 4 4
Check students' writing.
5 4
5 4

10
The groups of elbows, spirals, and ziti should be colored.
Check students' drawings.

11
6 5 6
5 6 5
Check students' writing.
5 6
6 5

12
The groups of pots, vases, and tulips should be circled.
Check students' drawings.

13
7 7 7
6 6 6
Check students' writing.
6 7
7 6

14
The groups of lemons, cherries, and oranges should be circled.
Check students' drawings.

15
7 7 7
8 8 7
Check students' writing.
8 7
7 8

16
The groups of pens, erasers, and crayons should be circled.
Check students' drawings.

17
8 9 9
8 8 9
Check students' writing.
9 8
9 8

18
The groups of clouds, moons, and umbrellas should be circled.
Check students' drawings.

19
9 10 10
9 9 10
Check students' writing.
10 9
9 10

20
Check students' work.
Check students' work.

21
Check students' work.
11 12
10 11

22
Check students' work.
13 11
14 12

23
Check students' work.
14 16
15 13

24
Check students' work.

25
Check students' work.
16 15
17 18

26
Check students' work.
20 19
18 17

27
3 5
14 16 18
12 14 16
7 9 11
8 10 12 14 16 18
4 13 9 8 6
10 18 14 19 5
16 11 17 12 15

28
1 ten 1 one 1 ten 2 ones
1 ten 4 ones

1 ten 7 ones 1 ten 8 ones
1 ten 9 ones

2 tens 0 ones 2 tens 1 one
2 tens 2 ones

2 tens 3 ones 2 tens 5 ones
2 tens 6 ones

2 tens 7 ones 2 tens 9 ones
3 tens 0 ones

29
10 11 12
13 15 19
20 21 22
23 27 30

30
29 30 31
34 35 38
39 40 41
44 45 48

31
Check students' work.
Check students' work.

32
49 50 53
54 55 56
59 60 62
64 65 68

33
69 70 73
79 80 87
89 90 92
95 97 99

34
Check students' work.

35
3¢ 5¢
8¢ 7¢
5¢ 7¢
9¢ 10¢

36
12¢ 10¢
10¢ 15¢
10¢
15¢
19¢
20¢ 20¢

37
26¢ 29¢
25¢ 28¢
25¢
30¢
25¢ 30¢
35¢ 50¢

38
34¢
41¢
65¢
37¢
41¢
26¢
25¢
25¢

39
The following coins should be circled:
1 nickel, 1 dime
2 dimes, 1 nickel

1 dime, 2 nickels
1 nickel, 2 pennies

4 pennies
1 dime, 1 nickel, 2 pennies

1 quarter, 4 pennies
1 quarter, 1 dime, 1 nickel

40
15¢ 32¢
35¢ 30¢
10¢ 8¢
20¢ 27¢

41
Check students' work.

42
Check students' work.

43
Check students' work.

44
12 8
2 10 5
11 1 6

45
Check students' drawings.

46
9 8 1
5 7 10
12 3 4
6 6 2

47
Check students' drawings.

48
3 12 1
2 9 1
6 7 2
8 10 12

49
1. b 2. a 3. d 4. c
5. g 6. e 7. h 8. f
From left to right, watches should be brown, blue, green, purple, yellow, and red.

50
Check students' work.

51
Check students' work.

52
Check students' work.

53
Check students' work.
■ ■
▽ ▽
■ □

54
Check students' work.
3
5
6

55
1 kg 2 g
3 oz. 2 lb.
These items should be circled:
feather pencil
balloon paper

56
3
4
5
4
7
9

57
These items should be circled:
pitcher jug
taller jar 1 qt.
2 cups 2 pints
4 cups 4 cups

58
ruler: ribbon, board
liter: milk, juice
scale: apples, cheese

ruler: rope, crayon
clock: time child is waking, time school is out
scale: cookies, apples

59
7 6 6
5 5 4
8 4 1
2 3 9
6 8 7
4 5 9
7 9 8
7 9 2

60
8 10 6 9 10
11 13 11 10 11
11 10 10 12 11
13 13 15 14 12
14 12 12 16 15
16 13 14 17 18

61
2 3 2
7 3 2
1 1 3
2 5 1
5 4 1
2 4 6
9 8 3
5 6 7

62
3 5 9 4 6
7 5 4 8 6
5 7 3 7 9
9 9 4 8 4
8 7 6 7 6
8 9 8 9 9

63
3 6 8
12 1 ten 3 ones 3 tens 6 ones
41¢
Check students' work.
5 14
4 8

Page numbers are indicated in color.